Disney LEARNING

ENGLISH BRAIN BOOST

GRADE 3

NELSON

This workbook belongs to:

_____

Disney LEARNING

Published by Nelson Education Ltd.

ISBN-13: 978-0-17-685498-0
ISBN-10: 0-17-685498-3

Printed and bound in Canada
1 2 3 4 21 20 19 18

For more information contact Nelson Education Ltd.,
1120 Birchmount Road, Toronto, Ontario M1K 5G4.
Or you can visit our website at nelson.com.

Contents

Track Your Learning

START

1 2 3 4 5

26 25 24 23 22 21 20 19

27 28 29 30 31 32

53 52 51 50 49 48

54 55 56 57 58 59

77 76 75 74 73 72

78 79 80 81 82 83 84 85

Colour a circle for every completed activity
to finish the Brain Boost learning path!

6 7 8 9 10 11

18 17 16 15 14 13 12

33 34 35 36 37 38 39 40

47 46 45 44 43 42 41

60 61 62 63 64 65

71 70 69 68 67 66

86 87 88 89 90 FINISH

Word Ladder

Riley and Bing Bong love to rock out in their imaginary band. The crowd goes wild feeling the beat!

Start at the bottom of the word ladder. Solve the clues. Reach the top!

A sweet snack
Add one letter.
Change one letter.

Feel the beat and jump out of your _____!
Change one letter.

Clean and tidy
Change one letter.

Carnivores eat it.
Change one letter.

A fire gives this off.
Change one letter.

b e a t

HINT The words, from bottom to top, will be in alphabetical order. They rhyme, too.

Fill In the Blanks

Bing Bong meets Joy and Sadness in Imagination Land. He is excited to show them around.

Fill in each blank. Use the word that comes first, in alphabetical order.

1. Bing Bong is _____ (thrilled / tickled) to give Joy and Sadness a tour.

2. Joy and Sadness are _____ (amazed / awed) by the attractions.

3. _____ (Gigantic / Giant) French fries tower over them at the entrance.

4. Imagination Land has _____ (big / beautiful) flowers.

5. Joy _____ (loves / likes) the fluffy clouds in Cloud Town.

6. Sadness gets a _____ (trophy / ribbon) in Trophy Town.

7. Joy is _____ (shocked / surprised) to see the Imaginary Boyfriend Generator.

8. At the end of the tour, Joy and Sadness _____ (hurtle / hop) aboard the Train of Thought.

HINT When words start with the same letter, look at the second letter. Which letter comes first?

5

Maze

Hiro Hamada and Baymax are searching for the masked villain, Yokai.

Help Hiro and Baymax find the masked villain. Draw a path for them through the maze. At each intersection and word pair, follow the word that comes first alphabetically.

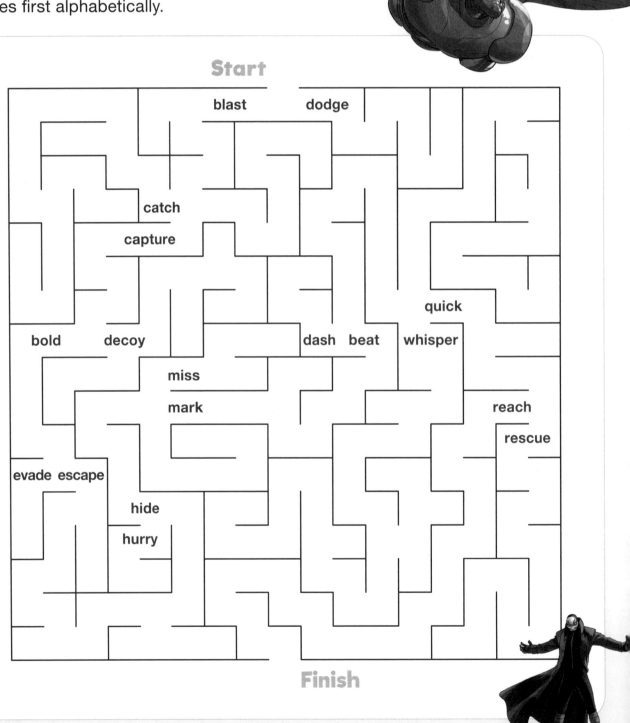

Start

blast   dodge

catch

capture

quick

bold   decoy   dash beat   whisper

miss

mark   reach

rescue

evade escape

hide

hurry

Finish

Crack the Code

Professor Callaghan has hurt people while trying to destroy his enemy.

Read the words in the Word Bank. Put those words in alphabetical order from **1** to **8**.

Use the first two letters of each word to crack the code. Put the letters in the space with the matching number.

Word Bank

gentle   Reach   home   rye

enter   toast   lonely   icicle

1. _____   5. _____

2. _____   6. _____

3. _____   7. _____

4. _____   8. _____

What lesson do we all need to remember?

_____ _____v_____ _____ _____ _____ is a _____ _____l_____ _____w
   6   1   2   3   5

v_____ _____ _____ _____ _____ _____.
  4   8   7

Word Blocks

Joy **sl**ips and falls into the Memory Dump. She **dr**ags Riley's core memories with her. Now Riley will **st**art to forget her most important moments!

The **purple** letters above form consonant blends. Fill in the word blocks using words from the Word Bank. These words all have consonant blends. Save Riley's precious memories!

1. ☐☐☐ ☐☐ ☐☐☐ across a ☐ ☐☐☐☐☐ pond makes Riley feel free.

2. The ☐☐☐ ☐☐ ☐☐ of her skates make marks on the ice.

3. Riley's parents are ☐ ☐☐☐ ☐ ☐☐ ☐☐ ☐☐ ☐☐ of her efforts during the hockey game.

4. Seeing ☐ ☐☐☐☐☐☐ ☐ on her pizza changes Riley's ☐ ☐☐☐ ☐ afternoon into something ☐ ☐☐☐☐☐ ☐☐ .

Word Bank

broccoli   dreadful

frozen   playoff

great   Skating

blades   proud

HINT When you say a word with a consonant blend, you can hear both letters.

Unscramble the Words

Sometimes **the** Emotions get all mixed up. **Th**ey don't **kn**ow **wh**at to do.

The **purple** letters above form **digraphs**. Unscramble the mixed-up words. Say each word. Listen to the sound of the digraph.

chere

_____

shtou

_____

wiph

_____

dkcu

_____

sheak

_____

wckre

_____

tinkh

_____

fshi

_____

wisthle

_____

mthoer

_____

HINT When you say a word with a consonant digraph, you hear only one sound. A digraph can appear at the beginning, middle, or end of a word.

Crossword

Baymax practises his karate skills by smashing a board.

Practise your word skills. Complete the crossword. Use words with blends and digraphs.

Across

2. you can do this with a rope

4. another word for fake

6. not deep

8. to take something that is not yours

10. a hint

11. fast

12. what you think with

Down

1. to pick out or select

3. someone who steals

5. to speak very quietly

7. a reward for winning

9. enough

Word Ladder

Big Hero 6 doesn't turn into a top superhero team overnight. The team practises hard to become a single, fighting force.

Start at the bottom of the word ladder. Solve the clues. Reach the top!

Superheroes who work together
Change two consonants.

You study for one.
Change one short vowel and one consonant.

To make something tip
Change one consonant.

Part of a sword
Change the vowel.

Stop.
Change one long vowel to a consonant.

An angel has one.
Change one long vowel and one consonant.

———————

———————

———————

———————

———————

———————

h   e   r   o

HINT A long vowel sounds like its letter name (the letter **i** in **fight**). A short vowel sound does not (the letter **i** in **fit**).

11

Crossword

Sadness has a short **a** sound. Fear has an r-controlled **e** sound.

Complete the crossword. Use your knowledge of vowel sounds. Some letters have been placed for you.

Across

1. a feeling with a short **a** sound
2. clothing with a long **o** sound
3. fall on ice with a short **i** sound
5. a meal with a short **u** sound
7. a colour with a short **e** sound
8. choo-choo vehicle with a long **a** sound

Down

1. opposite of **go** with a short **o** sound
3. a round shape with an r-controlled **e** sound
4. a colour with a long **u** sound
6. a young person with a long **i** sound

Word Search

A memory sphere changes from happy to sad depending on which Emotion touches it.

The letter **y** changes, too. Sometimes it is a consonant. Other times, it is a vowel.

In the word list, underline all the words that have **y** as a vowel. Then (circle) those words in the word search.

YOUTH	H	Y	B	N	C	N	Z	A	Z	N	O	X
GYM	Y	E	A	Q	M	M	M	Y	T	H	P	F
TRYING	M	R	P	D	P	O	Y	S	G	W	O	V
YELLOW	N	P	Y	H	Q	T	R	Y	I	N	G	W
HYMN	W	L	T	H	N	S	P	H	U	O	Y	T
YOUR	X	Y	A	U	G	H	X	I	U	P	A	X
WHY	J	J	E	X	H	E	N	N	Y	T	L	C
YULE	W	U	I	X	U	L	E	W	K	T	L	J
YAWN	K	R	M	I	G	Y	M	E	L	W	X	Y
SPY	M	Q	G	N	N	E	S	R	Q	S	W	X
SHYLY	W	U	E	G	W	J	N	N	Z	P	N	W
MYTH	W	H	Y	X	U	S	H	Y	L	Y	O	A

HINT The letter **y** sometimes sounds like a long or short **i**.

Unscramble the Words

Riley argues with her parents. Now, Family Island is dark and silent and beginning to crumble.

Island has a silent letter **s**. Unscramble the words with silent letters. Say each word. <u>Underline</u> the silent letter.

heston

_____

cbmo

_____

cstlea

_____

kcnok

_____

ykol

_____

gnemo

_____

mucles

_____

plubrem

_____

weerh

_____

sgni

_____

HINT Each scrambled word starts with the correct letter.

Fill In the Blanks

Jangles the Clown smashes his way through Dream Productions! Riley's dream turns into a nightmare.

If you were in Riley's dream, what would you do? Complete each word. Choose the correct silent letter.

1. I would try to g_____ess (u / h / a)

   what is _____rong (t / w / l) with Jangles.

2. I would try to ca_____m (w / u / l) him down.

3. I would ask Jangles w_____y (h / i / u) he is angry.

4. I would lis_____en (k / t / s) to Jangle's reasons.

5. I would _____rap (w / p / g) up a present for him.

6. I would offer him a bisc_____it. (n / u / s)

7. I would _____nit him a colourful scarf. (g / k / p)

8. I would play a song on the g_____itar. (l / a / u)

9. I would take Jangles to a beautiful i_____land. (s / u / g)

10. I would not _____now what to do. (k / s / g)

11. I would leave the s_____ene (l / h / c) quickly!

12. It is not the _____our (h / c / p) anyone wants to be awake!

Crack the Code

Tadashi and his friends go to the San Fransokyo Institute of Technology. Hiro is amazed at what they learn.

Crack the code. Find out what topics they learn about.

Letter Code

a	b	c	d	e	f	g	h	i	j	k	l	m
1	2	3	4	5	6	7	8	9	10	11	12	13

n	o	p	q	r	s	t	u	v	w	x	y	z
14	15	16	17	18	19	20	21	22	23	24	25	26

1. Wasabi studies _____ _____ _____ _____ _____ _____.
                                 13   1   20   20   5   18

2. Go Go Tomago studies how

    _____ _____ _____ _____ _____ _____ _____ can be used to
    13   1   7   14   5   20   19

    move objects.

3. Honey Lemon studies

    _____ _____ _____ _____ _____ _____ _____ _____ _____.
    3   8   5   13   9   3   1   12   19

4. Tadashi studies the

    _____ _____ _____ _____ _____ _____ _____ _____ _____ _____
    19   20   18   21   3   20   21   18   5   19

    of robots.

HINT All the words connect to science and technology.

Word Blocks

Hiro can build almost any type of structure with microbots. He can build walls, bridges, platforms, and more.

Fill in the word blocks. Use the words in the Word Bank. Underline one fact you learn about structures.

Word Bank

forces   strong   form   stable   compression

load   shape   tension

1. To be useful, structures must be ⬚⬚⬚⬚⬚

   and ⬚⬚⬚⬚⬚⬚.

2. Useful structures can support a ⬚⬚⬚⬚, or weight, placed on them.

3. A structure's ⬚⬚⬚⬚ or ⬚⬚⬚⬚⬚ can make it stronger.

4. A structure must stand up against ⬚⬚⬚⬚⬚⬚ that are

   always acting on it, including ⬚⬚⬚⬚⬚⬚⬚⬚⬚⬚⬚

   and ⬚⬚⬚⬚⬚⬚⬚.

HINT All the words connect to structures. Think about the clues in each sentence. The clues can help you figure out what any new words mean.

Unscramble the Words

Joy and Bing Bong sing in order to blast their wagon rocket into the air. Their singing **propels** the rocket.

Unscramble the **purple** words. Make words related to force and movement.

1. **Moevtmen** _____ is another word for

   motino _____.

2. **Feorc** _____ is a push or a pull that changes an object's motion.

3. **Fnrictio** _____ is a force that **solws** _____ down an object's motion.

4. **Garvtiy** _____ is a force that **pllus** _____ objects together.

5. The **erengy** _____ of an object in motion is known as

   kintice _____ energy.

6. **Mgatens** _____ can move some objects without even touching them!

HINT Each scrambled word starts with the correct letter.

Maze

Riley stick-handles her way around many challenges in hockey. Her parents cheer for her every single time.

Follow the sports words from Start to Finish. Celebrate a big win!

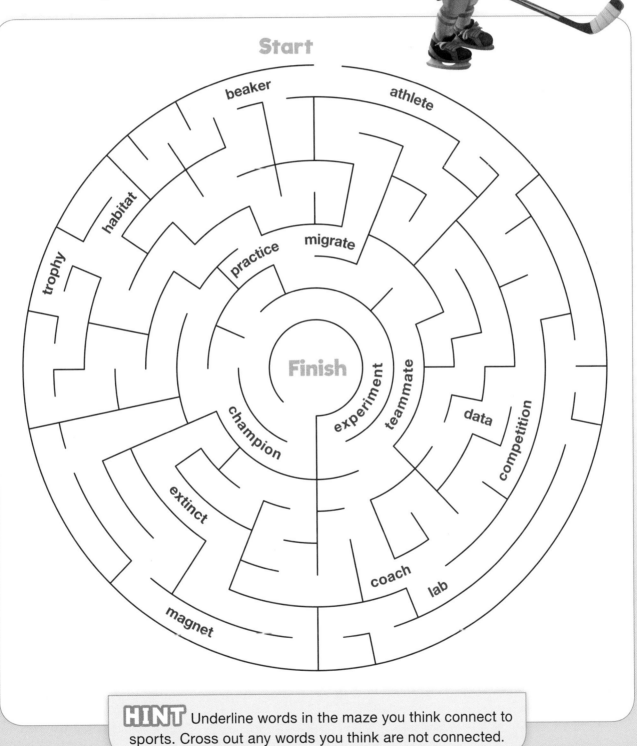

Start

beaker

athlete

habitat

trophy

practice

migrate

Finish

experiment

teammate

champion

data

competition

extinct

coach

lab

magnet

HINT Underline words in the maze you think connect to sports. Cross out any words you think are not connected.

19

Solve the Riddles

The Big Hero 6 team lives in San Fransokyo. It is a modern, multicultural community.

Solve the riddles. Use the words in the Word Bank. Learn more about communities. <u>Underline</u> one fact you learn about communities.

Word Bank

rural   community   suburb   citizen   urban

1. What do you call a group of people who live in the same place or

   share the same interests, or both? _____

2. What do you call a country-like setting without many buildings,

   people, or traffic? _____

3. What do you call a place where tall buildings stand side by side

   with many people living in them? _____

4. What do you call an area with many homes that is just outside a city?

   _____

5. What is a name for a person who has a vote that gives them a voice

   in their country? _____

Crossword

Hiro lives in the city with Aunt Cass. There are lots of things to do there.

Complete the crossword. Find out why people live where they do. Some letters have been placed for you.

Down

1. people live in them
2. the opposite of work time
3. used to grow crops and raise animals
4. coal, trees, water
6. factories and businesses that make goods or provide services
7. needed to earn money
8. liquid needed to live

Across

5. the general weather in an area over a long period of time
9. the number of people living in an area
10. cars, buses, trains, planes

HINT To figure out clues you find challenging, think about the letters you already know.

21

Word Blocks

Riley does not like broccoli on her pizza! But is broccoli on pizza a crime against food? Or is it just a great way to eat your veggies?

Fill in the word blocks. Use the words in the Word Bank. Underline one fact you learn about nutrition.

Word Bank

sugar   calcium   fat   vitamins   fruits   grains   minerals

1. Healthy foods include ☐☐☐☐☐☐ , vegetables,

and whole ☐☐☐☐☐☐ .

2. These foods have a lot of ☐☐☐☐☐☐☐☐ and

☐☐☐☐☐☐☐☐ , which your body needs to be healthy.

3. For strong bones, you need lots of ☐☐☐☐☐☐☐ , too.

4. Foods with a lot of ☐☐☐☐☐ , salt, and ☐☐☐ are

not healthy choices.

HINT Look at the number and shape of letters in each word.

Word Search

As a young girl, Riley loved making up stories with Bing Bong. A good story took them wherever they wanted to go.

In the word list, <u>underline</u> all the elements needed to make a good story. Then (circle) those words in the word search.

CHARACTER	D	I	A	L	O	G	U	E	P	E	S	X
DIALOGUE	L	O	I	M	A	G	E	R	Y	D	H	T
ESSAY	N	T	H	C	P	I	M	J	W	P	F	H
FACTS	E	M	G	Q	Y	K	H	C	M	L	V	E
IMAGERY	P	R	O	B	L	E	M	Y	Z	O	L	M
METAPHOR	M	E	T	A	P	H	O	R	O	T	S	E
NUMBERS	S	R	Q	H	C	Y	O	Z	Z	D	E	Y
PLOT	I	V	J	V	S	O	L	U	T	I	O	N
PROBLEM	M	Y	S	T	Q	Z	M	E	E	E	Y	Z
REALITY	I	S	E	T	T	I	N	G	P	L	O	J
SETTING	L	T	C	H	A	R	A	C	T	E	R	A
SIMILE	E	G	C	J	X	G	O	A	Y	N	E	J
SOLUTION												
THEME												

HINT Look for words both across and down.

Solve the Riddles

Why does Hiro want to go to SFIT? Because it's a **cool school**! When you answer a riddle with a clever, two-word rhyme, it's called a **hink pink**.

Use your rhyming skills. Complete the hink pinks!

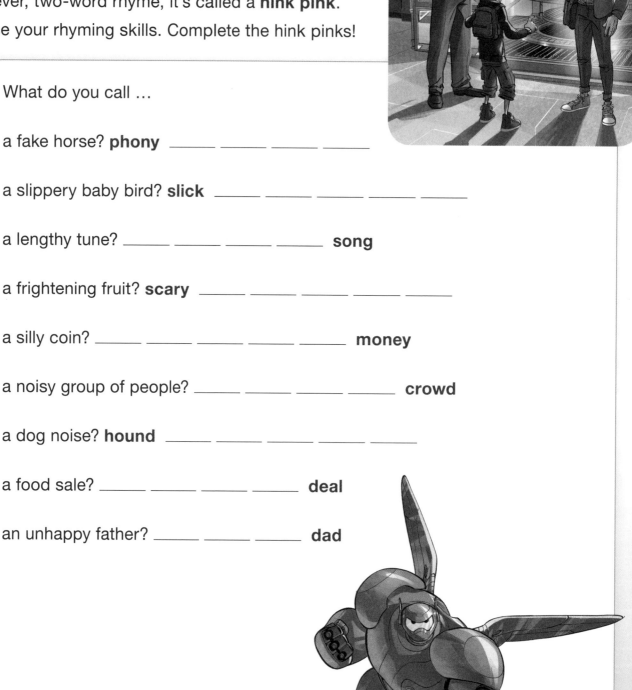

What do you call …

a fake horse? **phony** _____ _____ _____ _____

a slippery baby bird? **slick** _____ _____ _____ _____

a lengthy tune? _____ _____ _____ _____ **song**

a frightening fruit? **scary** _____ _____ _____ _____

a silly coin? _____ _____ _____ _____ _____ **money**

a noisy group of people? _____ _____ _____ _____ **crowd**

a dog noise? **hound** _____ _____ _____ _____ _____

a food sale? _____ _____ _____ _____ **deal**

an unhappy father? _____ _____ _____ **dad**

HINT One word in each hink pink is usually a noun. The other word is usually an adjective.

Solve the Rebus

Baymax is trying to figure out what is wrong with Hiro. But he is missing some important pieces of information.

The rhyming poem is missing pieces, too. Use the picture clues to figure out what they are.

Baymax is a healing bot,

But Hiro's hurt is not what he  _____.

Hiro has a broken ♥ _____,

And helping it heal is Baymax's part.

Hiro's pain can't be healed in one 🌙 _____.

It'll take some time for him to feel all right.

First aid won't mend or heal his  _____.

Friendship and love is what it will take.

> **HINT** Sometimes the endings of rhyming words are spelled the same way (**day, may**) and sometimes they are not (**day, weigh**).

Unscramble the Words

When Joy is in charge, Riley is happy.
When Sadness is in charge, Riley is unhappy.
Happy and **unhappy** are opposite pairs.

Unscramble the opposite pairs.

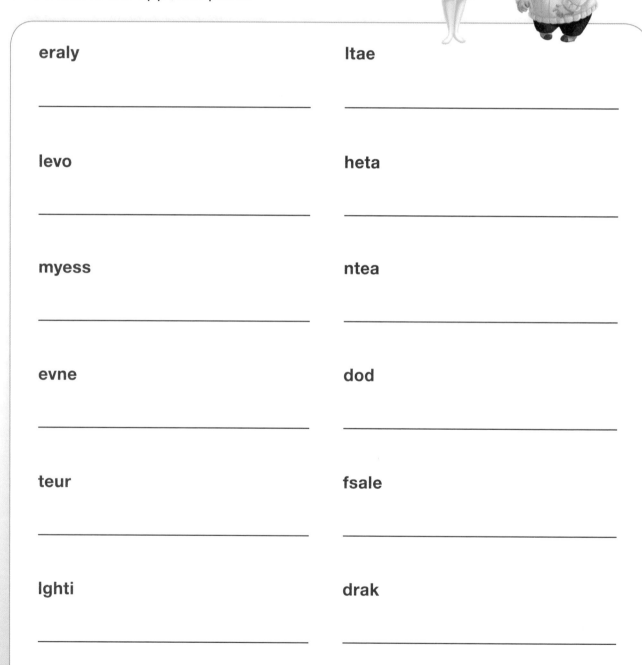

eraly	ltae
_____	_____
levo	heta
_____	_____
myess	ntea
_____	_____
evne	dod
_____	_____
teur	fsale
_____	_____
lghti	drak
_____	_____

HINT If you can unscramble one part of an opposite pair, it will help you unscramble the other part. So, if you get stumped, work on the other word.

Solve the Riddles

Joy finally understands one of life's riddles: there can't be **happiness** without **sadness**.

Fill in the missing opposite word for each riddle.

1. Without feeling **scared**, you can never feel **b**_____ _____ _____ _____.

2. Before you can be **awake**, you must first be **a**_____ _____ _____ _____ _____.

3. If we are not **together**, we must be **a**_____ _____ _____ _____.

4. Before you can **end**, you must **b**_____ _____ _____ _____.

5. It can't be **opened** if it's never been **c**_____ _____ _____ _____ _____.

6. Rain never falls **up**, but it always falls **d**_____ _____ _____.

7. If you're not **excited**, you might be **c**_____ _____ _____.

8. A path that is the opposite of **wide** is **n**_____ _____ _____ _____ _____.

9. If it doesn't taste **sour**, it may be **s**_____ _____ _____ _____.

10. If the glass is **full**, it can't be **e**_____ _____ _____ _____.

11. If you're not **inside**, you're **o**_____ _____ _____ _____ _____.

12. The opposite of **north** Is always **s**_____ _____ _____ _____.

HINT Each answer is the opposite of the purple word in the riddle.

Maze

Hiro and Baymax are flying around San Fransokyo, but now it is time to go home!

Draw their path through the maze and back to Hiro's room. Follow the base words with the prefix **re-**. <u>Underline</u> each base word.

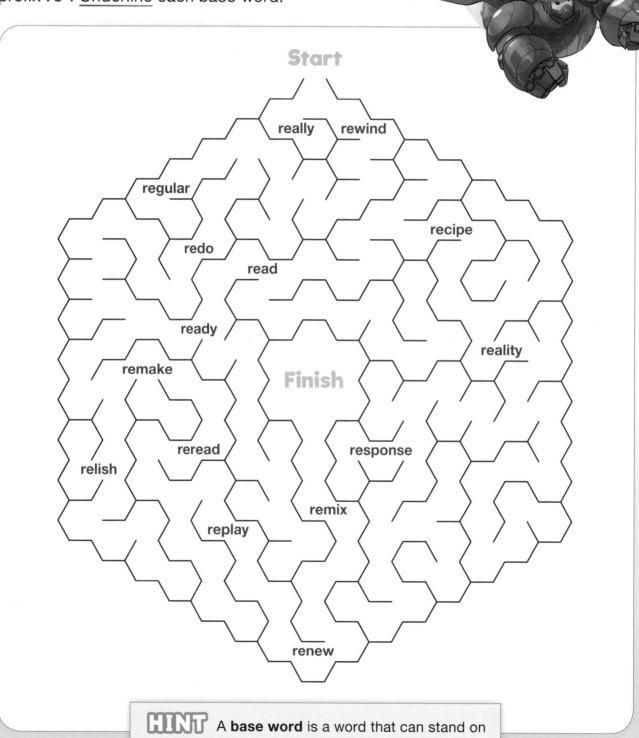

HINT A **base word** is a word that can stand on its own, without a prefix or a suffix (**write**, **visit**).

Fill In the Blanks

Aunt Cass is **dis**appointed when she must get Hiro and Tadashi out of jail.

Fill in the missing prefixes. Find out how the boys landed behind bars.

1. Hiro was _____**honest** at a robot fight. **(dis- / un- / re-)**

2. He lost the first match on purpose, then asked for a _____**match**. **(dis- / un- / re-)**

3. His opponent, Yama, was very _____**happy** about losing the second match. **(dis- / un- / re-)**

4. Yama asked Hiro to _____**turn** his money, but Hiro refused. **(dis- / un- / re-)**

5. Yama wanted to fight. Hiro was _____**sure** of how to escape. **(dis- / un- / re-)**

6. Tadashi rescued Hiro on his scooter, and they _____**appeared** into the night. **(dis- / un- / re-)**

7. The police caught them. The officers were _____**interested** in their story and took them to jail. **(dis- / un- / re-)**

8. _____**fortunately**, Aunt Cass had to go to the police station to get the boys out! **(Dis- / Un- / Re-)**

HINT Look at the word and the rest of the sentence to decide which prefix fits.

Unscramble the Words

Riley is in a bad mood, and her parents don't know why.

Unscramble the words to find out what's going on.

1. Riley **dkilesis** _____ her new home. It seems small and spooky.

2. She discovers pizza in San Francisco has broccoli on it.

   Unlievablebe _____!

3. Her parents try to **resureas** _____ her that everything will be okay.

4. Riley **dsigreesa** _____!

5. She is **urenus** _____ about all the changes in her life.

6. Their move to San Francisco can't be

   udnoen _____.

7. Maybe Riley can **rthinek** _____ her bad mood.

8. It is **unulsua** _____ for Riley to be acting this way.

HINT Each word begins with the prefix **un-**, **dis-**, or **re-**. Check each scrambled word for the prefix letters.

Crossword

Joy is cheer**ful** while Sadness is cheer**less**.

Suffixes like **-ful** and **-less** can change the meaning of base words.

Complete the crossword. Use your knowledge of suffixes. Some letters have been placed for you.

Across

1. full of beauty
2. full of hope
6. to make simple
8. up for debate
9. without harm
10. having sense

Down

1. without blame
3. full of wonder
4. full of power
5. without thanks
7. without fear

Crack the Code

Crack the code. Find out about Baymax's adventures. <u>Underline</u> the suffix in each word.

Letter Code

a	b	c	d	e	f	g	h	i	j	k	l	m
1	2	3	4	5	6	7	8	9	10	11	12	13

n	o	p	q	r	s	t	u	v	w	x	y	z
14	15	16	17	18	19	20	21	22	23	24	25	26

1. Baymax is the ___ ___ ___ ___ ___ ___ ___ superhero.
   2 9 7 7 5 19 20

2. Almost everyone is ___ ___ ___ ___ ___ ___ than Baymax.
   6 1 19 20 5 18

3. Baymax wants to cure Hiro's

   ___ ___ ___ ___ ___ ___ ___.
   19 1 4 14 5 19 19

4. But a broken heart is the ___ ___ ___ ___ ___ ___ ___
   thing to cure.
   8 1 18 4 5 19 20

5. It may be a while before Hiro experiences

   ___ ___ ___ ___ ___ ___ ___ ___ ___ again.
   8 1 16 16 9 14 5 19 19

Who will help heal Hiro's broken heart?

HINT Write out all the boxed letters in a row. This will help you unscramble the word.

Fill In the Blanks

It takes Hiro weeks to make thousands of microbots. You just need to add an **-s** to turn a single microbot into many microbots.

Turn each singular word into a plural word. Add an **-s** or **-es**.

1. At first, Hiro thinks Tadashi and his

   friend_____ are nerds.

2. After seeing their **project**_____ at the lab, though,

   he realizes they are cool **scientist**_____.

3. Well, everyone but Fred, who just reads **comic**_____ and eats

   invisible **sandwich**_____.

4. Hiro believes they can be **hero**_____. He designs special suits

   based on their **interest**_____.

5. Fred **wish**_____ for a suit that can breathe fire and do super jumps.

6. The suits have **weapon**_____. The team practises using them on

   different **target**_____.

7. After many **mistake**_____ and **miss**_____, the team knows

   how to use their **suit**_____ perfectly.

HINT Add an **-es** to singular words that end in **-ch, -sh, -s,** or **-ss** (**lunches, dishes, buses, losses**) to make them plural.

Maze

Joy and Sadness are lost in Long Term Memory. They need to get back to Headquarters fast.

Draw their path through the maze back to Headquarters. Follow the correctly spelled plurals.

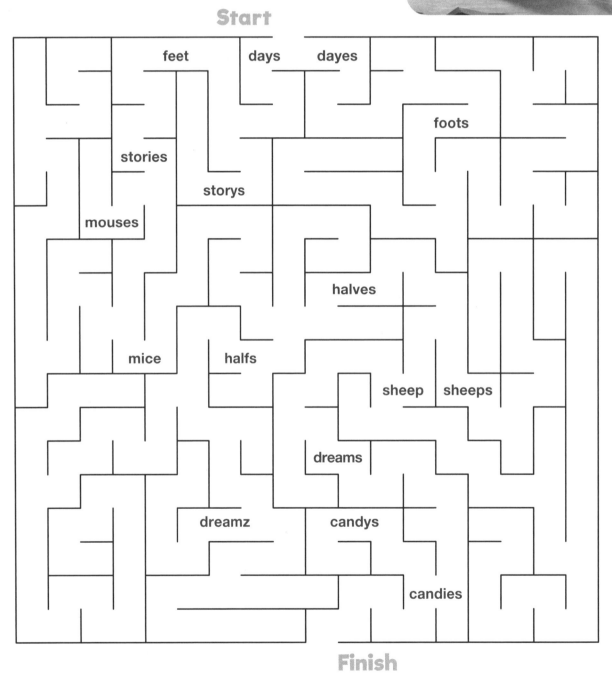

Start

feet days dayes

foots

stories

storys

mouses

halves

mice halfs

sheep sheeps

dreams

dreamz candys

candies

Finish

HINT Not all words become plural by adding an **-s** or **-es**. And sometimes, when a word ends in a consonant **y**, the **y** becomes an **i** and **-es** is added.

Word Blocks

Riley starts playing hockey when she is young. She learns to follow the rules of the game.

There are rules to follow when making a singular word plural. But some words don't follow the rules! You can't just add an **-s** or **-es** to make them plural.

Fill in the word blocks. Make each singular word plural.

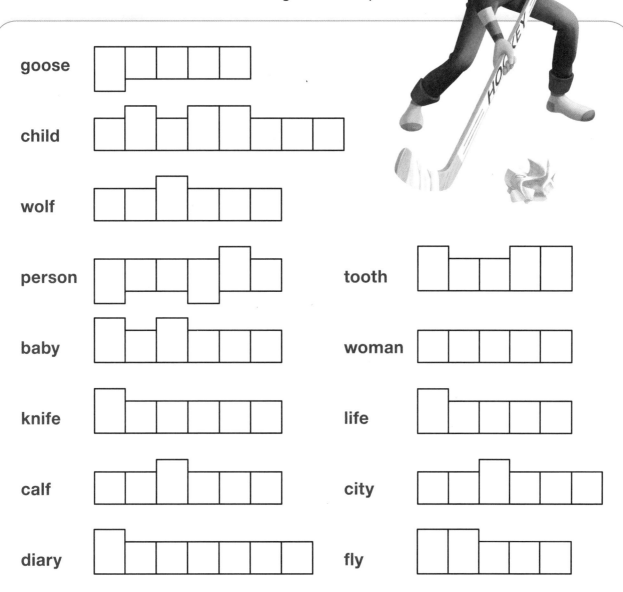

goose

child

wolf

person   tooth

baby   woman

knife   life

calf   city

diary   fly

HINT In each word block, pay attention to the height of the letters.

35

Crossword

Baymax is a **caregiving** robot. **Caregiving** is a compound word. (Circle) the two smaller words in caregiving.

Complete the compound-word crossword puzzle. Some letters have been placed for you.

Across

1. marks your spot in a book
3. a paste for cleaning teeth
5. not anywhere
7. a drop of water that falls from the sky
9. the day a person is born
10. a round object made of packed snow

Down

2. time of day after 12:00 p.m.
4. every single thing
6. Saturday and Sunday
8. a small, cup-sized cake

Crack the Code

Hiro is working hard. He wants to invent something new and exciting, but he keeps hitting dead ends.

Crack the code. Complete each compound word. Find out ways that could help Hiro have a breakthrough.

Letter Code

a	b	c	d	e	f	g	h	i	j	k	l	m
1	2	3	4	5	6	7	8	9	10	11	12	13

n	o	p	q	r	s	t	u	v	w	x	y	z
14	15	16	17	18	19	20	21	22	23	24	25	26

1. Hiro could have a good **break**___ ___ ___ ___ and

      6   1   19 20

   write ideas in a **note**___ ___ ___ ___.

    2   15   15   11

2. Maybe he could soak in the ___ ___ ___ ___**tub** to relax

    2   1   20   8

   and help his ideas flow.

3. Or pace around his **bed**___ ___ ___ ___.

    18   15   15   13

4. When he is about to give up, Tadashi flips him

   up___ ___ ___ ___ down.

    19   9   4   5

5. **Some**___ ___ ___ ___ ___ you just need to see things

    20   9   13   5   19

   in a new way!

Fill In the Blanks

The Train of Thought crashes! Joy, Sadness, and Bing Bong are all aboard.

To find out what happens next, look at the picture. Then write the action word in each sentence that best describes what is happening.

1. The train _____ (comes / glides / slams) to a halt.

2. Joy _____ (falls / dances / steps) from the train.

3. She _____ (crashes / rolls / stops) face first.

4. Bing Bong _____ (tumbles / tips / hops) out after her.

5. Sadness _____ (tiptoes / gets / leaps) to the ground next to them.

38

Fill In the Blanks

Disgust, Anger, and Fear are all very different inside and outside.

How different are they? Fill in the blanks to find out. Use the correct adjective from the Word Bank.

1. Disgust has _____ eyes

   with _____ lashes. Her

   _____ taste keeps her

   from trying _____ things.

Word Bank

long   green
gross   picky

2. Fear is _____ and

   skinny. His _____

   eyebrows are often scrunched with

   worry. His _____ nature

   makes him _____.

Word Bank

jumpy   bushy
tall   timid

3. Anger is stocky and

   _____. His skin

   is _____. His

   _____ head is a sign

   he is _____.

Word Bank

short   flaming
red   furious

Word Search

Aunt Cass's café is **bright** and **cheery**. It is a **comfortable** place to be.

The **purple** words above are adjectives. In the word list, <u>underline</u> adjectives that might also describe Aunt Cass's café. Then (circle) these words in the word search.

BUSY	Y	X	I	K	Q	R	E	M	I	D	Z	Y
CLEAN	Y	B	Z	J	U	N	G	R	E	E	N	K
COZY	Z	W	O	G	B	J	A	C	I	F	Q	G
CROWDED	V	I	B	B	L	D	I	W	D	F	N	W
DARK	S	W	E	E	T	V	R	C	R	R	N	E
DIRTY	J	M	X	A	K	G	U	L	H	I	U	L
FRIENDLY	T	T	I	D	Y	B	S	E	K	E	P	C
GREEN	M	T	O	J	A	I	T	A	O	N	Y	O
INVITING	D	W	G	S	O	F	W	N	E	D	J	M
MESSY	N	I	N	V	I	T	I	N	G	L	C	I
SCARY	X	H	S	F	D	J	C	O	Z	Y	C	N
SWEET	B	G	G	J	F	U	M	V	Z	J	B	G
TIDY											
WELCOMING											

HINT Look for words that run across and down.

Word Blocks

Oh no! Go Go drives off the end of the pier. She didn't **see** the **sea**!

See and **sea** are homophones. These words sound the same but look different. Homophones also have different meanings.

Complete each sentence. Fill in the word blocks. Use the correct homophone pair.

Word Bank

night blew won knot knight weak

not heal one heel blue week

1. He felt ⬚⬚⬚⬚ after being sick for a ⬚⬚⬚⬚.

2. She wanted the doctor to ⬚⬚⬚⬚ her sore ⬚⬚⬚⬚.

3. He ⬚⬚⬚⬚ out the ⬚⬚⬚ candles on his birthday cake.

4. He is ⬚⬚⬚ able to untie the tiny ⬚⬚⬚⬚.

5. She competed in only ⬚⬚⬚ race and ⬚⬚⬚ it!

6. The ⬚⬚⬚⬚⬚⬚ stayed up all ⬚⬚⬚⬚⬚.

HINT Use the Word Bank for extra help.

Solve the Riddles

Why does Riley steal her mom's credit card and run away? She wants to **buy bye**.

Solve each hink pink. Write the correct homophone pair.

1. What do metal thieves do?

   steal _____

2. What does a female deer shop with?

   _____ **dough**

3. What do you call a stinky chicken? A **foul** _____

4. What do you call a colourless bucket? A _____ **pail**

5. What do you call a dull pig? A _____ **boar**

6. How does a rabbit line its nest? With **hare** _____

7. What did the detective ask the wizards? _____ **witch** is guilty?

8. What do you call a fancy hotel room?

   A _____ **suite**.

9. What do you call a boring jet?

   A **plain** _____.

HINT Think about the meaning and spelling of each homophone.

Word Search

Many of Riley's memories are headed for the Memory Dump.

The word list contains memories that Riley may not want to lose. <u>Underline</u> the two-syllable words. Then (circle) those words in the word search.

BALLOONS

BALLS

BASEBALL

BLOCKS

BROCCOLI

CRAYONS

FRIENDS

GIFTS

PARTIES

ROCKET

SINGING

TOYS

UNICORN

WAGON

```
J  Z  E  Y  B  F  M  I  O  R  Z  W
R  R  R  O  K  K  E  T  C  A  E  A
O  R  F  F  P  A  R  T  I  E  S  G
C  F  B  I  N  C  V  Z  X  C  J  O
K  E  D  D  P  J  V  D  B  H  F  N
E  K  C  X  T  S  I  N  G  I  N  G
T  Q  R  B  L  S  V  E  C  B  C  O
T  P  A  S  U  L  G  I  N  G  R  K
E  X  Y  B  A  L  L  O  O  N  S  V
K  J  O  K  R  W  K  L  X  J  B  X
K  U  N  Z  C  A  A  G  O  N  E  C
B  A  S  E  B  A  L  L  Z  G  A  Z
```

HINT Say each word. Clap for each syllable you hear. Underline the words you clap twice for.

Maze

Oh no! Baymax is lost in a maze of alleys. Hiro needs to find him!

Draw Hiro's path through the alleys to Baymax. Follow the three-syllable words.

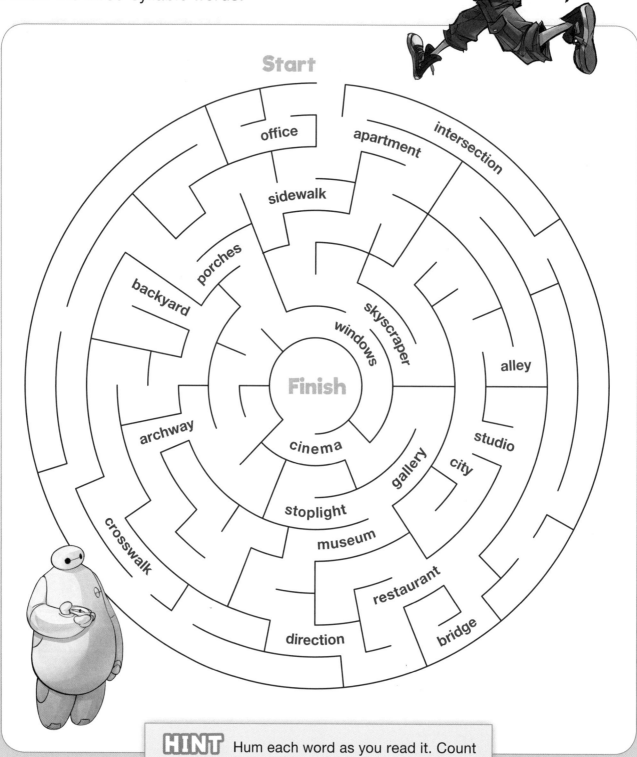

Start

office   apartment   intersection

sidewalk

porches

backyard

skyscraper

windows

alley

Finish

archway

cinema

studio

gallery   city

stoplight

museum

crosswalk

restaurant

direction   bridge

HINT Hum each word as you read it. Count the number of hums. One hum = one syllable.

Fill In the Blanks

Baymax doesn't always understand idioms. Someone says, "You gave me a heart attack!" and he tries to give first aid. The idiom really means "You surprised me!"

Help Baymax by completing these definitions for common idioms. Fill in the missing words. Use the words in the Word Bank.

Word Bank

secret   easy   attention   ignore

certain   trouble   common   sick

1. When something is a piece of cake, it's _____.

2. When someone is under the weather, they are _____.

3. When someone is in hot water, they are in _____.

4. When someone is all ears, they are paying _____.

5. When someone spills the beans, they share a _____.

6. When something is in the bag, it is _____.

7. When something is a dime a dozen, it is _____.

8. When you give someone the cold shoulder, you

_____ them.

HINT An **idiom** is a group of words where its meaning is different than the individual words it contains.

Solve the Rebus

Anger is so mad he is **blowing his top**! For most people, though, "blowing your top" is just an expression, or idiom.

"A picture is worth a thousand words" is another idiom. In this puzzle, a picture is worth one word. Fill in each missing word. Complete each idiom.

1. When I'm in a good mood, I'm on top

   of the _____.

2. When I lose my nerve, I get cold 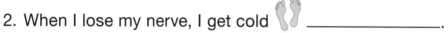 _____.

3. When I can't sit still, I've got  _____ in my pants.

4. When I feel out of place, I feel like a _____

   out of _____.

5. When something is unlikely, I say it will happen

   when _____ fly.

6. When I believe something silly, my brother says

   I fell for it _____, line, and sinker.

7. When I have a serious conversation with my friend,

   it is called having a _____ to _____.

Crossword

Fear is **as timid as a mouse**. Anger is **as bold as brass**.

Similes like these are used so often we can sometimes finish their endings without thinking.

Finish the similes. Complete the crossword. Some letters have been placed for you.

Across

1. swims like a

2. cries like a

3. runs like the

5. as pale as a

6. as cool as a

8. as red as a

9. as brave as a

Down

1. as light as a

4. as hard as a

7. as cute as a

HINT A simile compares two things using the words **like** or **as**.

Silly Sentences

Baymax thinks **a cat is like a hairy baby.** That's a silly simile!

Finish the sentences. Write your own silly similes.

1. Hiro is as smart as _____.

2. His brain is like _____.

3. Go Go is as fast as _____.

4. Wasabi's hands are like _____.

5. Fred is usually as calm as _____.

6. In his fire-breathing super suit, Fred is like

_____.

7. Aunt Cass is as patient as _____.

8. Honey is as happy as a _____.

9. She can also be as tough as _____.

10. Baymax is as gentle as a _____.

11. He can also be as strong as _____.

12. Tadashi was as brilliant as _____.

13. Abigail is as brave as _____.

Word Blocks

Fred learns a lot from comic books, such as **superheroes are to good as villains are to evil.** This comparison is called an analogy.

Fill in the word blocks so each analogy makes sense. Use the words in the Word Bank.

Word Bank

page   drive   flower   laughing   kitten

plane   vegetable   sadness   puppy   Apple

1. Petal is to ☐☐☐☐☐☐ as ☐☐☐☐ is to book.

2. Fly is to ☐☐☐☐☐ as ☐☐☐☐☐ is to car.

3. Crying is to ☐☐☐☐☐☐☐ as

☐☐☐☐☐☐☐ is to happiness.

4. Dog is to ☐☐☐☐☐ as cat is to ☐☐☐☐☐☐.

5. ☐☐☐☐☐ is to fruit as broccoli is to

☐☐☐☐☐☐☐☐☐.

HINT Analogies describe the relationship between things. Think about each relationship described in the analogy.

Fill In the Blanks

Sadness and Joy are opposite emotions.
Crying is to Sadness as laughing is to Joy.
That analogy uses opposites.

Fill in the blanks. Complete each analogy.
Use the opposites in the Word Bank.

Word Bank

sweet   day   shallow   quiet   hard
small   snow   cold   sour   big   river

1. Shout is to **loud** as whisper is to _____.

2. Moon is to **night** as sun is to _____.

3. Rabbit is to **soft** as rock is to _____.

4. Lake is to **deep** as puddle is to _____.

5. **Hot** is to summer as _____ is to winter.

6. **Lemon** is to _____ as **strawberry**

   is to _____.

7. **Mouse** is to _____ as **elephant** is to _____.

8. **Ski** is to _____ as **raft** is to _____.

Silly Sentences

What happens when Joy and Sadness wake up a sleeping Jangles? The **clown causes chaos**!

Use alliteration to make the silliest sentences seem possible. Read your sentences out loud.

1. Sadness _____ _____ and sighs.
                            verb beginning with **s**   noun beginning with **s**

2. Joy _____ _____ and jiggles.
               verb beginning with **j**   adverb beginning with **j**

3. _____ Anger _____ and accidentally
     adjective beginning with **a**   verb beginning with **a**

   _____.
     verb beginning with **a**

4. Disgust _____ _____, but doesn't
              verb beginning with **d**   adverb beginning with **d**

   _____.
     verb beginning with **d**

5. Fear fumbles _____ and _____
                  noun beginning with **f**   verb beginning with **f**

   feet-first!

HINT A noun names a person, place, or thing. A verb is an action word. An adjective describes a noun. An adverb describes an action.

Solve the Riddles

Baymax keeps his friends afloat after they crash into the water. He is a **brave bobbing bot**.

Solve the riddles. Use alliteration. The answers are pretty punny!

1. What do you call a plant with a sense

   of humour? f____nn____ fl____ ____ ____ ____

2. What do you call an annoying insect?

   b____gg____ ____g b____g

3. What is a body of water that's so wealthy it has two banks?

   r____ ____h r____v____r

4. What do you call a colt that has lost its voice?

   ho____r____e h____r____e

5. What do you call a feline that repeats everything?

   c____p____ c____ ____

6. What do you call a happy rodent?

   c____ip____ ____r ch____ ____m____ ____k

7. What do you call a snoozing reptile?

   l____z____ l____z____ ____d

Crossword

Prof. Callaghan is Tadashi's favourite teacher. **Prof.** is an abbreviation for **Professor.**

Complete the crossword. In the puzzle, write the full word for each abbreviation. Some letters have been placed for you.

Across

4. Mon.

5. Jr.

6. Dr.

7. m

8. Sept.

9. Sat.

Down

1. kg

2. Sr.

3. Sgt.

6. Dec.

Unscramble the Words

Riley is off on an imaginary journey. The Emotions are trying to read the map to find out where Riley is headed.

Help the Emotions understand the map. Unscramble the geography words. Then write the abbreviation for each word. Look at the abbreviations in the Word Bank for extra help.

Word Bank

E Mt. N Rd. km S Ave. Hwy W

nroth _____

sothu _____

kioletrem _____

roda _____

esta _____

hiwaygh _____

mtonu _____

wste _____

avnuee _____

Word Search

Anger gets angry when Riley can't have dessert. He also gets angry when he sees Riley's new house. Saying Anger is angry all the time is repetitive.

Underline the synonyms for **angry** in the list. Then circle them in the word search.

BITTER	B H E E S O R E T O K O
CONFUSED	U L F D X R E H T U S R
CROSS	E X U X C F P O M T A W
EMBARRASSED	C C R O S S W U W R R E
FUMING	K G I B I T H K M A E M
FURIOUS	Y B O M J M U F C G U P
GLEEFUL	E I U C K S F U M E Q B
HUFFY	C T S D G A F M O D S F
JOLLY	P T R K F P Y I D G Q O
MAD	I E Q F W C F N C Y Y T
OUTRAGED	S R O W D Q Q G H B B V
SCARED	C L Y J B C H S G M A D
SORE	
WORRIED	

HINT **Synonyms** are words that have the same or similar meanings.

Crossword

When they wear their super suits, the members of Big Hero 6 are more intense versions of themselves. Go Go is normally quick, but she is speedy in her super suit.

Complete the crossword. For each **purple** word, identify a synonym.

Across

1. The heroes are **smart**.

5. The Big Hero 6 team is **brave**.

6. Callaghan becomes their **enemy**.

7. The members of Big Hero 6 are **friends**.

9. Callaghan's actions could **ruin** the city.

10. Fred is sometimes **goofy**.

Down

2. Baymax is very **caring**.

3. Fred's family is **rich**.

4. Hiro and Baymax **save** Callaghan's daughter.

8. The team must **fight** Callaghan to save the city.

Word Blocks

There**'s** no time to lose! If Hiro and Baymax don**'t** hurry, Yokai**'s** going to catch them.

Speed up their escape! Turn the **purple** words into contractions. Write the correct contraction in each word block.

1. Yokai is evil! **He is** ⬚⬚,⬚ sending his microbots after Hiro and Baymax.

2. **It is** ⬚⬚,⬚ time to run, Baymax!

3. Baymax **is not** ⬚⬚⬚,⬚ designed to move fast.

4. **They will** ⬚⬚⬚,⬚⬚ never escape at that speed!

5. **They had** ⬚⬚⬚,⬚ better think of something—fast!

6. **They are** ⬚⬚⬚,⬚ going to have to jump out a window.

7. **It is** ⬚⬚,⬚ the only way to get free.

8. Phew! **They have** ⬚⬚⬚⬚,⬚⬚ escaped.

57

Picture Search

Riley is unhappy in San Francisco. She plans to run away back to Minnesota, but she isn't sure she should.

Look at the pictures. Predict which picture shows the next part of the story. Circle your choice.

What helped you make your prediction?

_____

_____

_____

_____

_____

_____

HINT Making predictions can help you think about the story and understand it.

Crack the Code

Bing Bong and Joy need to get back to Headquarters. They want to stop Riley from running away. But Bing Bong is stuck in the Memory Dump!

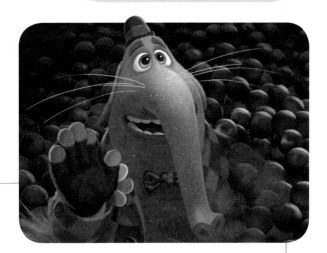

What do you think happens next?
Why do you think so?

_____

_____

Now, crack the code. Find out if your predictions were accurate.

Letter Code

a	b	c	d	e	f	g	h	i	j	k	l	m
1	2	3	4	5	6	7	8	9	10	11	12	13

n	o	p	q	r	s	t	u	v	w	x	y	z
14	15	16	17	18	19	20	21	22	23	24	25	26

Bing Bong waves goodbye. He tells Joy to take Riley to

the _____ _____ _____ _____ for him.
    13   15   15   14

Joy _____ _____ _____ _____ _____ _____ to Headquarters
    18   21   19   8   5   19

to _____ _____ _____ _____ Riley.
   19   1   22   5

> **HINT** Can you predict what the word will be after you fill in the first couple of letters?

Fill In the Blanks

Tadashi and Hiro have a close relationship. They know each other well.

Read the story to learn more about the brothers. Pay attention to the details so you can answer the questions on page 61.

> Tadashi is worried about his little brother, Hiro. Hiro is smart, but he wastes his time on robot fights instead of going to school.
>
> Tadashi wants to show Hiro there are better things to do. After a robot fight, he takes Hiro to the robotics lab at SFIT. Tadashi is a student there.
>
> Hiro is amazed by the lab and all the cool subjects Tadashi is studying. Hiro feels inspired!
>
> When they leave the lab, Hiro cannot stop talking about how much he wants to be accepted as a student at SFIT.

How does Tadashi feel about Hiro's robot-fighting? How do you know?

_____

_____

_____

Where does Tadashi take Hiro? Why there?

_____

_____

_____

HINT As you read, underline key details about the characters.

What does Hiro think of the lab at Tadashi's school?

_____

_____

_____

Do you think Tadashi is a good older brother? Why?

_____

_____

_____

Out of Order

Read the story about Riley's move to San Francisco. Pay attention to the story events so you can retell the story in order on page 63.

When Riley's dad gets a new job in San Francisco, Riley's heart sinks. San Francisco is in California—far away from where they live in Minnesota.

Soon after, Riley's parents sell their home and pack up all their belongings. Next, they drive toward California. Riley is excited when she sees San Francisco's famous Golden Gate Bridge.

Her excitement vanishes later on when she sees where they will live. It is a small, dark home squished into a long row of other small, dark homes.

Riley misses her old friend Meg. Riley talks to Meg on her laptop, but Riley gets mad when Meg mentions a new friend. Riley slams her laptop shut.

Number the pictures from **1** to **4** to retell the story in order.

Riley's new home is small, dark, and squished.

Riley's mom and dad sell their home in Minnesota.

Riley and her parents drive to San Francisco.

Riley is mad when her old friend Meg mentions a new friend.

Fill In the Blanks

Look at the picture. Read the story about the mystery man in the lab.
Pay attention to information about the characters and events.

The Big Hero 6 team wants to catch the man in the mask. They follow him
to an abandoned lab, where they find old videos from security cameras.

The videos show a group of people touring the lab. Some are wearing
white lab coats while others wear military uniforms. One man wears an
expensive blue suit. He's in charge.

The man boldly announces that history will be made. He orders the
scientists to start two teleportation portals. They hesitate because it looks
like there might be a problem with one of the portals. The man tells them
to continue anyway.

Seconds later, disaster strikes. One portal explodes and the video screens
go dark.

Complete each sentence. Find out more about the mystery
man from page 64. Use the words in the Word Bank.

Word Bank
cares   billions   proud   wealthy   money   important

1. The man in the expensive suit owns a company that spent

   _____ of dollars.

2. So, he must be _____.

3. The man is _____ of the portals and wants to
   show them off.

4. Because the portals cost a lot of _____, he ignores
   warnings that they may be unsafe.

5. So, money must be more _____ to him than safety
   or people.

6. The Big Hero 6 team remembers something Professor Callaghan

   said about Alistair Krei: he _____ more about money
   than safety.

Who do you think the mystery man is?

_____

Crack the Code

Read the story about Riley and Bing Bong's trip.
Then answer the questions on page 67.

Riley and Bing Bong want to take their band on tour. They decide to go to Australia. Riley has heard that many interesting animals live there.

They pack snacks for their trip and climb into their wagon rocket. They count down to launch: five … four … three … two … one!

Nothing happens.

Uh-oh. Why won't the rocket start? It needs fuel! Bing Bong says the rocket runs on song power, so they start singing as loudly as they can.

The rocket rolls forward and picks up speed. Riley and Bing Bong fly out the window and across the ocean toward Australia!

Use information from the story on page 66
to answer the questions.

1. Where do Riley and Bing Bong go on tour?

    ___ ___ ___ ___ ☐ ___ ___ ___

2. What vehicle do they use to travel?

    ___ ☐ ___ ___ ___ ☐ ___ ___ ___ ___

3. What do Riley and Bing Bong bring with them on their trip?

    ___ ___ ___ ___ ☐ ___

4. What does the rocket need to start?

    ___ ___ ___ ☐

5. What do they do to fuel the rocket?

    ☐ ___ ___ ___

Unscramble the boxed letters to answer the question.

What animals will Riley and Bing Bong see in Australia?

Kangaroos, wallabies, and ___ ___ ___ ___ ___ ___

Solve the Rebus

Solve the Rebus. Write the correct words in the blank spaces.

Riley is _____ sitting a boy named Devan. They aren't

getting along at first.

Devan wants a _____, but Riley says no. She's made

them for her friend. The little boy stamps his _____.

Big _____ roll down his cheeks. Riley has

an _____.

She remembers her **1st** _____ time on

_____. She kept falling. Her parents sat her

_____ on a bench. Her dad sprinkled _____

on her head. With a _____, he called her a hothead.

He said she needed to cool _____. That made her laugh

and she tried skating again.

HINT Some of the pictures use an image of a homophone for the word that is
needed. For example, rebus puzzles often use the number **8** for the word **ate**.

Riley tells Devan the) _____. She pretends

to sprinkle ❄ _____ on his head. He laughs.

Devan is ready to play a 🎲 _____ with Riley.

The 🍐 _____ of them have so much

🎉 _____ playing together!

Crossword

Read the story about how Big Hero 6 became a superhero team.

Hiro makes amazing super suits for his friends.

Hiro makes Baymax a suit of armour with rocket thrusters so he can fly. He then makes Fred a fire-breathing, super-jumping monster suit. He makes laser gloves for Wasabi and a portable chemical factory for Honey Lemon's purse. For Go Go, Hiro makes super-fast running discs.

Hiro makes himself a suit with super-strong magnets. The magnets connect with Baymax's suit, so Hiro can hang on while they fly.

The team practises for hours in their suits. There are accidents. Honey Lemon covers the yard in chemical goo, Baymax shoots his rocket arm through a wall, and Fred sets the lawn on fire.

But eventually, the team is ready to fight Yokai. Big Hero 6 is born!

Complete the crossword. Use information from the story on page 70. Some letters have been placed for you.

Across

2. his super suit has laser gloves
3. the reason why Baymax can fly
5. inside Honey Lemon's purse is a …
8. the name of the superhero team
9. enemy of Big Hero 6

Down

1. Hiro's super suit contains these
4. Hiro makes one for each of his friends
6. wearer of the fire-breathing suit
7. the fastest runner on the team

HINT Reread the story. Underline key words, such as **fast** or **suit**.

Silly Sentences

An explosion destroys the Tech Showcase at SFIT. The blast blows out doors and windows.

The sentences below are knocked around. Put the words back in order so the sentences make sense.

1. out A fire breaks during the Tech Showcase.

   _____

2. make Tadashi and Hiro it outside.

   _____

3. still inside is Professor Callaghan.

   _____

4. to save his teacher into the burning building Tadashi runs.

   _____

   _____

5. still inside is Tadashi when an explosion destroys it.

   _____

   _____

6. Tadashi and is dies Hiro heartbroken.

   _____

HINT Remember, sentences begin with capital letters. Try arranging the words in different combinations until you get a combination that makes sense.

Fill In the Blanks

Hiro and Baymax have had a busy night! What have they been up to?

Fill in the blanks. Look at the words before and after the blank space to figure out which word is missing. Use the words in the Word Bank for extra help.

Word Bank

tiptoe   attacks   finds   losing

microbot   police   escape   microbot

1. Hiro _____ a _____ in his pocket.

2. The _____ leads Hiro and Baymax to a warehouse.

3. Suddenly, the masked villain Yokai _____ them.

4. Hiro and Baymax run away. They barely _____.

5. They try to tell the _____, but no one believes them.

6. At home, they _____ past Aunt Cass and up to Hiro's room.

7. Baymax is _____ air fast!

Fill In the Blanks

The Emotions are at the control panel. Things are not going well! What is happening?

Fill in the missing end punctuation to find out. Use the punctuation from the box.

1. The Emotions are a mess_____

2. They watch as Riley misses the puck at

   hockey tryouts_____

Punctuation

? ! .

3. Why is this happening_____

4. Anger is so frustrated he wants to scream_____

5. Who can help Riley_____

6. She'll be so sad if she doesn't make the team_____

7. What if they distract her_____

8. Then she can take a breath and calm down_____

9. Will their plan work_____

10. Can they do enough to help Riley succeed at tryouts_____

11. They need to try something_____

12. What do you think happened_____

HINT Many questions begin with **who, what, where, why, when,** and **how.**

What's Missing?

During hockey tryouts, Riley is angry, frustrated, and annoyed. She yells, throws her stick, and stomps off the ice.

If you were Riley's friend, what would you say to her? To get some ideas, fill in the missing commas.

Hi Riley. Are you okay? I'm sorry that tryouts were so hard frustrating and difficult.

What do you think happened? Did you trip fall and lose your balance?

Maybe your skate laces ripped broke or came untied.

Sometimes people have terrible horrible bad days.

My worst day was when I was late for school forgot my homework and spilled red juice on my shirt.

It must be hard to move to a new city leave your friends and go to a new school.

Would it help if we talked about it Riley? You can yell shout and cry!

Let's hang out! I will make sure to have snacks drinks and good music.

HINT Commas separate a series of words or ideas. They show pauses in sentences. Use commas when speaking to a person.

What's Missing?

Abigail Callaghan will be the first person to teleport. She might be saying, "This is amazing!"

Fill in the missing quotation marks. Find out what happens during Abigail's test run.

Ready to go for a ride, Abigail? asks Alistair Krei.

Abigail checks her seatbelt and controls in the pod one

last time. She says, We've invited all these people. Might as

well give them a show.

Abigail flips a few switches and settles back against her seat. Then,

a technician spots a problem.

The General asks, Mr. Krei, is there a problem?

Krei replies, No. No problem. It's well within the parameters.

Let's move forward.

The countdown begins. The cabin pressure is a go and the pod is engaged.

The technician shouts, Field breach!

They lose all contact with the pod. The pilot is gone.

HINT Use quotation marks before and after someone speaks.

Silly Sentences

Abigail is lost and alone in the portal. Will she be trapped forever?

Imagine you were in the portal with Abigail. What would you be thinking? Finish the sentences. Use the punctuation from the box.

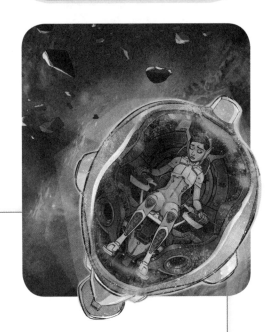

Punctuation

, . ? " "

What _____

_____

_____

How will _____

_____

_____

I have an idea! Maybe if we _____

_____

_____

Solve the Riddles

Riley's dad makes her laugh. He goofs around, makes funny faces, and tells corny jokes.

Solve the funny riddles. Fill in the missing letters to complete the nouns. <u>Underline</u> the other nouns in the riddle.

1. What has hands but cannot clap?

   cl_____ _____ _____

2. What gets wetter the more it dries? **t**_____**w**_____ _____

3. What's something you must keep after you give it?

   p_____ _____**m**_____ _____ _____

4. What's full of holes but still holds water? **s**_____ _____ _____**ge**

5. What has a floor but is not a room? **o**_____ _____**a**_____

6. What flies all day but never lands? **fl**_____ _____

7. What can you catch but never throw? **c**_____ _____**d**

8. Who can shave all day but still have a beard? **b**_____ _____**b**_____ _____

9. What must you break before you can use it? **e**_____ _____

10. What is full of keys but can't open doors? **p**_____ _____ _____**o**

11. What has one eye but can't see? **ne**_____**d**_____ _____

HINT A noun names a person, place, or thing.

Word Ladder

Joy and Bing Bong are stuck at the bottom of the Memory Dump.

Build a noun ladder from the bottom to the top. Solve the clues. Save Joy and Bing Bong!

___ ___ ___ ___

A place to shop
Change one letter.

___ ___ ___ ___

You throw it.
Change one letter.

___ ___ ___ ___

A male cow
Change one letter.

___ ___ ___ ___

Tulips and onions before they bloom
Change two letters.

___ ___ ___ ___

A goose _____ shows you are cold.
Change one letter.

___ ___ ___ ___

You may get one in your throat if you're about to cry.
Change one letter.

d   u   m   p

Maze

Oh no! **Aunt Cass's** cat, **Mochi**, is wandering away from the **Lucky Cat Café**.

The **purple** words above are proper nouns. Follow the proper nouns. Draw a path for Aunt Cass through the maze. Find Mochi!

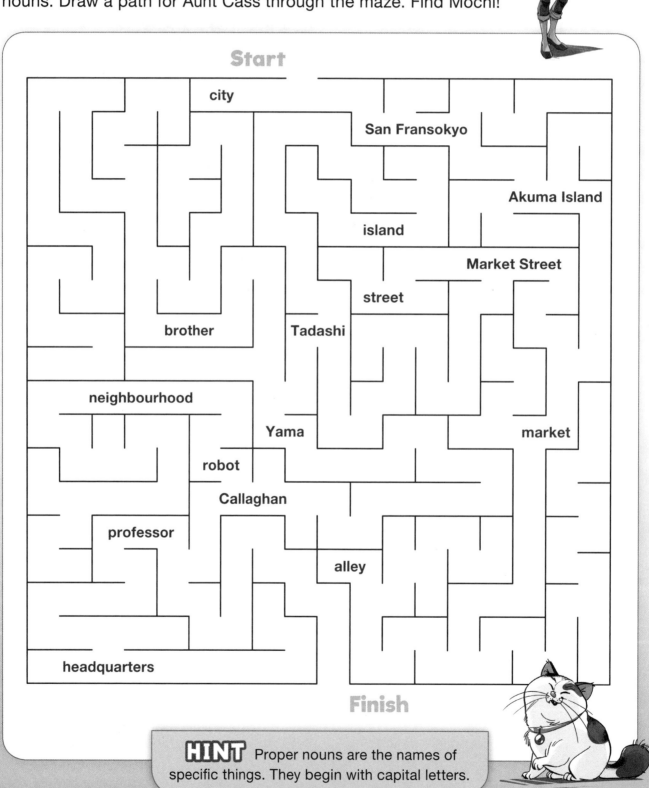

Start

city

San Fransokyo

Akuma Island

island

Market Street

street

brother   Tadashi

neighbourhood

Yama   market

robot

Callaghan

professor

alley

headquarters

Finish

HINT Proper nouns are the names of specific things. They begin with capital letters.

Silly Sentences

Tadashi builds Baymax, a nursing robot, because he wants to help people.

If you could build a robot, what would it do? How would you introduce it to people?

Hello! I am _____, a _____
                    your name   adjective

scientist and inventor.

I am unveiling _____, the most _____
                      proper noun   adjective

robot ever created.

More powerful than _____!
                          proper noun

_____ is designed to _____
      proper noun   verb

on _____.
        noun

It can also _____ into a _____.
                  verb   noun

Life in _____ will never be the same!
              place name

HINT Make your story as silly as possible. Fill in the words before reading the rest of the sentence.

81

Fill In the Blanks

Riley's mom has something important to tell her about their move to San Francisco.

Fill in the missing verbs. See what Riley's mom wants to say. Use the words from the Word Bank.

Word Bank

announces   explains   is   saying

enters   settles   surprises   thanks

1. Riley's mom _____ _____ _____ _____ _____ _____ Riley's bedroom.

2. Riley _____ _____ ready to hear more bad news, but her mom

_____ _____ _____ _____ _____ _____ _____ _____ her.

3. Her mom _____ _____ _____ _____ _____ _____ _____ on the floor beside Riley's sleeping bag.

4. She _____ _____ _____ _____ _____ _____ _____ _____ that she is very proud of Riley.

5. She _____ _____ _____ _____ _____ _____ _____ _____ that she has noticed how hard Riley is trying to be happy in their new home.

6. She _____ _____ _____ _____ _____ _____ Riley before

_____ _____ _____ _____ _____ _____ good night.

HINT Look at the number of letter spaces for each word.

Crack the Code

One of Riley's special memories is the first time she **skated**. She **wobbled** and **slipped** on the ice.

The **purple** words above are past tense verbs.

Crack the code to discover the past tense verbs that make up more of Riley's memories.

Letter Code

a	b	c	d	e	f	g	h	i	j	k	l	m
1	2	3	4	5	6	7	8	9	10	11	12	13

n	o	p	q	r	s	t	u	v	w	x	y	z
14	15	16	17	18	19	20	21	22	23	24	25	26

1. When Riley _____ _____ _____ _____ _____ _____ broccoli for the first
   20   1   19   20   5   4

   time, she thought it was disgusting.

2. When she _____ _____ _____ _____ _____ _____ her first goal, it was
   19   3   15   18   5   4

   the most exciting thing ever.

3. Riley _____ _____ _____ _____ _____ playing with Bing Bong in their
   12   15   22   5   4

   imaginary band.

4. She _____ _____ _____ _____ _____ _____ the pots and pans like drums.
   16   12   1   25   5   4

5. When Riley _____ _____ _____ _____ _____ with her friend Meg,
   10   15   11   5   4

   she _____ _____ _____ _____ _____ _____ _____ so hard.
   12   1   21   7   8   5   4

HINT The past tense of a verb is often formed by adding **-ed** or **-d** (when the words end in an **e**).

Crossword

The Big Hero 6 team is tense! They don't know if they'll be able to outsmart Yokai and his mind-controlled microbots.

Complete the crossword. Figure out which verb tense is needed. Some letters have been placed for you.

Across

2. This year, I _____ eight years old. **(am / was)**

4. My friend _____ me today. **(call / called)**

5. Last year, I _____ seven years old. **(am / was)**

6. Last week, I _____ karate. **(try / tried)**

Down

1. Yesterday, I _____ to school. **(walk / walked)**

2. Today, we _____ having spaghetti for dinner. **(are / were)**

3. Today, I _____ a quarter. **(lose / lost)**

5. My birthday _____ last month. **(is / was)**

Maze

Baymax **kept** following the microbot through the city. Finally, he **found** where it wanted to go—a warehouse full of microbots.

Draw Baymax's path to the warehouse. Follow the irregular present tense verbs. Say the past tense form of each verb in the maze. Figure out if it is irregular or regular.

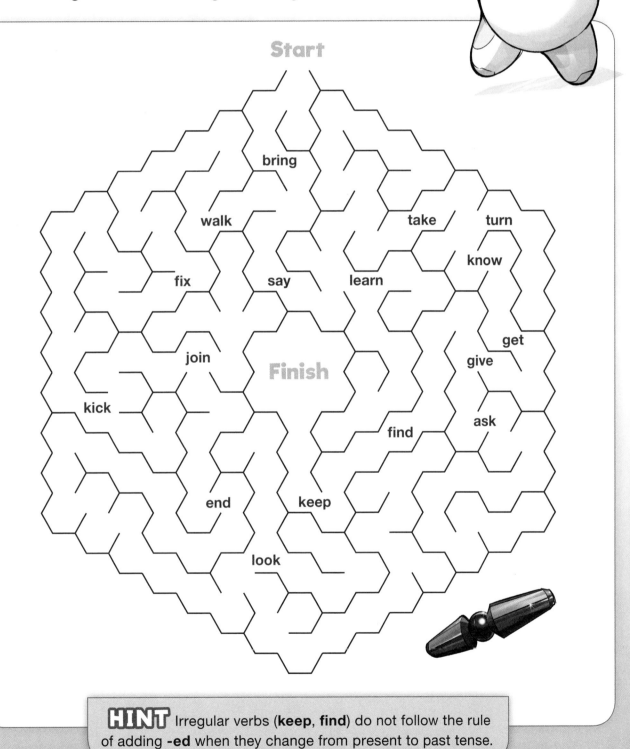

Start

bring

walk   take   turn

know

fix   say   learn

get

join   give

Finish

kick   ask

find

end   keep

look

HINT Irregular verbs (**keep**, **find**) do not follow the rule of adding **-ed** when they change from present to past tense.

Crossword

Sadness touches a **yellow** memory sphere, and it turns **blue**. She changes a **happy** memory into a **sad** one.

The **purple** words above are adjectives.

Complete the crossword. Use adjectives. Some letters have been placed for you.

Across

7. a bright, cloudless day and a happy mood

8. something that cannot be done

10. how skunks and dirty socks smell

Down

1. kind, with a soft touch

2. someone who is only a few years old

3. when someone wants to know more, they are

4. how you feel when you haven't eaten

5. doesn't want to get out of bed

6. a place that gives you goosebumps is ...

9. _____ as a fox (rhymes with **fly**)

Silly Sentences

In Minnesota, Riley has five Islands of Personality. They are Family, Honesty, Hockey, Friendship, and Goofball Islands. When she moves to San Francisco, she gains more islands!

What Islands of Personality do you have? Complete each sentence. Make your islands as silly as possible.

_____ has a very _____ mind.
    your name   adjective

It's not surprising that _____ _____ Island
                         adjective   noun

is one of the biggest Islands of Personality.

That's because _____ is _____ and
              your name   adjective

_____.
  adjective

_____'s _____ heart helped create a
    your name   adjective

new island called _____ Island.
               adjective

That sounds so _____!
           adjective

HINT To make your sentences as silly as possible, fill in the words before reading the rest of the sentence.

Word Blocks

There are many ways to compare the members of Big Hero 6. Hiro is **younger** than the others. He is also **smaller**. Fred is **goofier** than the rest of the team.

The **purple** words above are comparative adjectives. Fill in the word blocks to complete each comparison. Use the words in the Word Bank.

Word Bank

bigger   calmer   faster   softer   quieter   sweeter

1. Wasabi is ⬜⬜⬜⬜⬜ than the others.

2. Go Go runs ⬜⬜⬜⬜⬜⬜ than her teammates.

3. She is also one of the ⬜⬜⬜⬜⬜⬜ members of the team.

4. Honey is ⬜⬜⬜⬜⬜⬜ than almost anyone.

5. Baymax's puffy body makes him ⬜⬜⬜⬜⬜⬜ than everyone else.

6. The rest of the team is ⬜⬜⬜⬜⬜ than Go Go, who loves a thrill.

HINT Comparative Adjectives describe two things (**younger**, **goofier**).

Unscramble the Words

Honey is tall. Wasabi is taller. Baymax is **tallest**.

Tallest is a superlative adjective. Unscramble the words. Write the correct superlative adjectives.

1. She is the **fstaest** _____ runner on the track team.

2. He is the **lestoud** _____ whistler in class.

3. August was the **httoest** _____ month of the year.

4. It is the **hppaites** _____ day of his life.

5. She lives in the **biusest** _____ city in the country.

6. The poodle was the **nciste** _____ dog in the group.

7. He is the **steb** _____ friend he has ever had.

8. I am the **shrtoest** _____ person in my family.

9. That is the **hghesti** _____ mountain in the world.

10. The orange kitten is the **smestall** _____ of the litter.

11. She is the **bvarset** _____ person I know.

12. That was the **esaiest** _____ quiz I ever took!

HINT Superlative adjectives describe three or more people, places, or things (**strongest**, **worst**)

89

Word Search

Joy is **accidentally** caught in a vacuum tube! The other Emotions watch **helplessly** as Joy **frantically** tries to free herself.

The **purple** words above are adverbs. An adverb describes an action or adjective. In the word list, <u>underline</u> the adverbs. Then ⟮circle⟯ those words in the word search.

CAREFULLY	L	O	U	D	L	Y	B	Z	S	V	S	V
EASILY	B	U	S	L	O	W	L	Y	U	F	V	K
JUMP	U	L	B	C	Q	T	V	R	D	X	I	X
LOUDLY	C	F	T	N	R	X	Y	A	D	N	J	A
NEAT	A	E	H	E	I	Q	V	W	E	E	X	J
NERVOUSLY	R	K	T	J	J	U	I	A	N	R	H	G
QUIETLY	E	Q	I	W	G	I	V	A	L	V	H	O
READ	F	P	R	S	O	E	G	D	Y	O	I	K
RUN	U	X	E	I	F	T	L	F	P	U	I	V
SING	L	J	D	C	Q	L	K	V	L	S	G	M
SLOWLY	L	R	L	E	U	Y	J	W	N	L	A	H
SUDDENLY	Y	B	Y	E	A	S	I	L	Y	Y	G	V
TALK												
TIREDLY												

Word Blocks

Riley is **lonely** in her new school. She **always** ate lunch with Meg back in Minnesota. **Now**, Riley stares **sadly** at her lunch and doesn't feel like eating.

The sentences below are lonely without their adverbs. Fill in the word blocks with words from the Word Bank. Complete each sentence.

Word Bank

Lately   quickly   fondly   Suddenly   excitedly   often   quietly

1. Riley dresses ☐☐☐☐☐☐☐ for school.

2. She thinks ☐☐☐☐☐☐☐☐☐ about making new friends.

3. She ☐☐☐☐☐ tells her class about life in Minnesota.

4. She says her family ☐☐☐☐☐ skated on the lake.

5. ☐☐☐☐☐☐☐☐ , things go horribly wrong.

6. She ☐☐☐☐☐☐ starts crying in front of everyone.

7. ☐☐☐☐☐ , everything seems to be going wrong!

Crack the Code

After soaring **through** the air **above** San Fransokyo, Baymax and Hiro take a break **on** a blimp.

The **purple** words above are prepositions. Crack the code. Reveal the missing prepositions. Find out where Hiro and Baymax have been.

Letter Code

a	b	c	d	e	f	g	h	i	j	k	l	m
1	2	3	4	5	6	7	8	9	10	11	12	13

n	o	p	q	r	s	t	u	v	w	x	y	z
14	15	16	17	18	19	20	21	22	23	24	25	26

1. Hiro daringly rides _____ _____ Baymax's back.
     15   14

2. They fly _____ _____ _____ _____ _____ _____ the city.
     1   18   15   21   14   4

3. They fly _____ _____ _____ _____ _____ _____ the bay.
     1   3   18   15   19   19

4. They soar _____ _____ _____ _____ San Fransokyo _____ _____
     6   18   15   13   20   15

   Akuma Island.

5. For fun, they swoop _____ _____ _____ _____ _____ the bridge.
     21   14   4   5   18

6. Then, Hiro and Baymax soar _____ _____ _____ _____ _____ _____ _____
     20   8   18   15   21   7   8

   clouds.

HINT Prepositions tell you where something is or where it is moving in relation to other objects.

Silly Sentences

Baymax isn't watching where he's going. He walks up the front of a car and then onto the roof of a truck. He ends up on top of a building!

If you went on a silly journey of ups and downs with a friend, where might you both end up? Fill in each blank. Use the Word Bank.

Word Bank

on   around   across   from   to   through   above
under   below   along   up   behind   into   out

_____ and _____ are deep in thought.
    your name   friend's name

They hop _____ a _____ without looking.
         preposition   noun

Luckily, they land _____ a slowly moving
              preposition

_____.
   noun

It carries them _____ a _____ before
         preposition   noun

dumping them _____ a _____.
         preposition   noun

They look _____ the _____ and
        preposition   noun

wonder how they ended up there!

Fill In the Blanks

Joy and Sadness work together to help Riley remember her core memories.

Conjunctions join words and ideas. Fill in each blank. Use **or**, **but**, or **and** to complete each sentence.

1. Riley tries to feel happy in San Francisco, _____ she misses her life in Minnesota.

2. She can stay and be unhappy _____ go back to Minnesota.

3. Riley starts to run away, _____ she changes her mind.

4. She stands up in the bus _____ tells the driver she wants to get off.

5. She loves her mom _____ dad too much to leave.

6. They hug _____ cry when she returns.

7. Riley and her parents feel sad because they miss their old life,

   _____ they are happy they are together.

8. Riley soon joins a hockey team _____ makes new friends.

9. If you moved to a new city, would you want to stay

   _____ go?

Unscramble the Words

Riley's life feels scrambled after her family moves to California. Nothing makes sense anymore.

Unscramble the words. Fill in the missing conjunctions. Make sense of the sentences.

1. The new house is small **adn** _____ dark.

2. Riley doesn't love her new room, **ety** _____ she tries to make the best of it.

3. Riley misses her dad **bseeauc** _____ he is always working.

4. Her parents can't cheer her up, **althouhg** _____ they try all the things that used to work.

5. Riley chats with her old friend Meg, **btu** _____ that makes things worse.

6. **Snice** _____ Meg has a new friend, Riley feels left out.

7. Riley is going to be very unhappy **unssel** _____ something changes.

8. She starts feeling better **arfte** _____ she learns it is okay to be sad.

9. Maybe Riley and her parents can be happy **wheverer** _____ they live as long as they are together.

Crack the Code

Baymax is a good caregiver. However, a few things must happen first before he can begin caregiving.

Crack the code. Find out what Baymax must do. Each sentence needs a sequence word. Then put the sentences in order by numbering them from **1** to **5**.

Letter Code

a	b	c	d	e	f	g	h	i	j	k	l	m
1	2	3	4	5	6	7	8	9	10	11	12	13

n	o	p	q	r	s	t	u	v	w	x	y	z
14	15	16	17	18	19	20	21	22	23	24	25	26

_____ _____ _____ _____, his suitcase unlatches and the lid opens.
  14   5   24   20

_____ _____ _____ _____ _____ _____ _____, he scans his patient
  6   9   14   1   12   12   25
and offers care.

_____ _____ _____ _____, Baymax begins filling with air.
  20   8   5   14

_____ _____ _____ _____ _____, Baymax hears an "ow!"
  6   9   18   19   20

_____ _____ _____ _____ _____ inflating, he can step forward and
  1   6   20   5   18
begin to help.

Fill In the Blanks

Hiro never gives up on his invention. Because of his determination, he and the microbots receive thunderous applause at the Tech Showcase.

Sadly, the person who wrote these rhymes gave up. Fill in the blanks to finish the rhymes. Use the words in the Word Bank.

Word Bank

easy   early   quit   roughest   blue

Just when things are at their toughest,

When your ideas are at their _____,

When you can't seem to make things fit,

It's the worst time for you to _____.

You have to push and struggle through,

Frustration, doubt, and feeling _____.

It won't be simple, fun, or _____,

In fact, it just might make you queasy.

But if you give up and quit too _____,

Chances are you'll fail big, surely.

Unscramble the Words

Riley is having a bad day. Her feelings are all mixed up and she loses her temper with her parents.

Unscramble the mixed-up words. Then use them to write a story about a bad day you had.

uspet _____   fendir _____

felgine _____   bretet _____

srory _____   tlkaed _____

_____

_____

_____

_____

_____

_____

_____

_____

Fill In the Blanks

Riley is experiencing many new things in San Francisco, such as walking to her new school by herself for her first day.

What would you do if you moved to a new city? Write a letter to a friend describing your new experiences.

Dear _____,
              name

               date

_____ are you? I am _____. Lately, I have
     question   adjective

been spending a lot of time _____. It is really
                                 verb

_____. In school, we are learning about _____,
    adjective   noun

_____, and _____.
    noun   noun

My favourite thing right now is _____ because
                               noun

_____.
                phrase to explain reason

Please write me back.

Sincerely,

_____
    your name

Answers

Word Ladder

Riley and Bing Bong love to rock out in their imaginary band. The crowd goes wild feeling the beat!

Start at the bottom of the word ladder. Solve the clues. Reach the top!

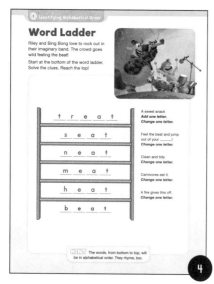

t r e a t	A sweet snack **Add one letter.**
s e a t	**Change one letter.** Feel the beat and jump out of your ____! **Change one letter.**
n e a t	Clean and tidy **Change one letter.**
m e a t	Carnivores eat it. **Change one letter.**
h e a t	A fire gives this off. **Change one letter.**
b e a t	

HINT The words, from bottom to top, will be in alphabetical order. They rhyme, too.

4

Fill In the Blanks

Bing Bong meets Joy and Sadness in Imagination Land. He is excited to show them around.

Fill in each blank. Use the word that comes first, in alphabetical order.

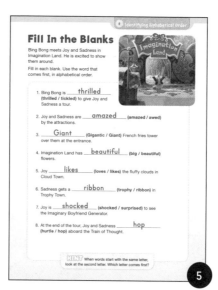

1. Bing Bong is __thrilled__ (thrilled / tickled) to give Joy and Sadness a tour.
2. Joy and Sadness are __amazed__ (amazed / awed) by the attractions.
3. __Giant__ (Gigantic / Giant) French fries tower over them at the entrance.
4. Imagination Land has __beautiful__ (big / beautiful) flowers.
5. Joy __likes__ (loves / likes) the fluffy clouds in Cloud Town.
6. Sadness gets a __ribbon__ (trophy / ribbon) in Trophy Town.
7. Joy is __shocked__ (shocked / surprised) to see the Imaginary Boyfriend Generator.
8. At the end of the tour, Joy and Sadness __hop__ (hurtle / hop) aboard the Train of Thought.

HINT When words start with the same letter, look at the second letter. Which letter comes first?

5

Maze

Hiro Hamada and Baymax are searching for the masked villain, Yokai.

Help Hiro and Baymax find the masked villain. Draw a path for them through the maze. At each intersection and word pair, follow the word that comes first alphabetically.

Start
blast → dodge
catch
capture
bold decoy → dash beat whisper → quick
miss → reach
mark → rescue
evade escape
hide
hurry
Finish

6

Crack the Code

Professor Callaghan has hurt people while trying to destroy his enemy.

Read the words in the Word Bank. Put those words in alphabetical order from 1 to 8.

Use the first two letters of each word to crack the code. Put the letters in the space with the matching number.

Word Bank
gentle Reach home rye
enter toast lonely icicle

1. enter
2. gentle
3. home
4. icicle
5. lonely
6. Reach
7. rye
8. toast

What lesson do we all need to remember?

R e v e n g e is a h o i l o w
v i c t o r y

7

Word Blocks

Joy slips and falls into the Memory Dump. She drags Riley's core memories with her. Now Riley will start to forget her most important moments!

The purple letters above form consonant blends. Fill in the word blocks using words from the Word Bank. These words all have consonant blends. Save Riley's precious memories!

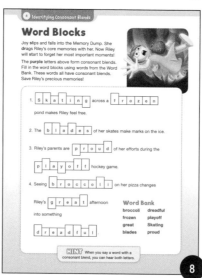

1. S k a t i n g across a f r o z e n pond makes Riley feel free.
2. The b l a d e s of her skates make marks on the ice.
3. Riley's parents are p r o u d of her efforts during the p l a y o f f hockey game.
4. Seeing b r o c c o l i on her pizza changes Riley's g r e a t afternoon into something d r e a d f u l.

Word Bank
broccoli   dreadful
frozen   playoff
great   Skating
blades   proud

HINT When you say a word with a consonant blend, you can hear both letters.

8

Unscramble the Words

Sometimes the Emotions get all mixed up. They don't know what to do.

The purple letters above form digraphs. Unscramble the mixed-up words. Say each word. Listen to the sound of the digraph.

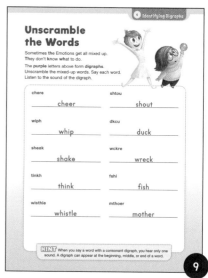

chere	cheer	shtou	shout
wiph	whip	dkcu	duck
sheak	shake	wckre	wreck
tinkh	think	fshi	fish
wisthle	whistle	mthoer	mother

HINT When you say a word with a consonant digraph, you hear only one sound. A digraph can appear at the beginning, middle, or end of a word.

9

Crossword

Baymax practises his karate skills by smashing a board.

Practise your word skills. Complete the crossword. Use words with blends and digraphs.

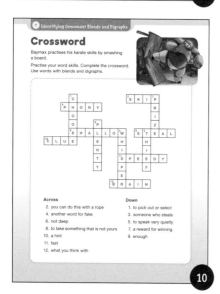

P H O N Y S K I P
S H A L L O W S T E A L
C L U E S P E E D Y
B R A I N

Across
2. you can do this with a rope
4. another word for fake
6. not deep
8. to take something that is not yours
10. a hint
11. fast
12. what you think with

Down
1. to pick out or select
3. someone who steals
5. to speak very quietly
7. a reward for winning
9. enough

10

Word Ladder

Big Hero 6 doesn't turn into a top superhero team overnight. The team practises hard to become a single, fighting force.

Start at the bottom of the word ladder. Solve the clues. Reach the top!

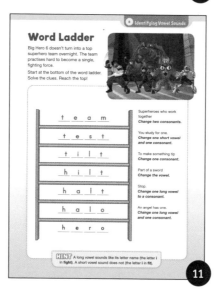

t e a m	Superheroes who work together **Change two consonants.**
t e s t	You study for one. **Change one short vowel and one consonant.**
t i l t	To make something tip **Change one consonant.**
h i l t	Part of a sword **Change the vowel.**
h a l t	Stop. **Change one long vowel to a consonant.**
h a l o	An angel has one. **Change one long vowel and one consonant.**
h e r o	

HINT A long vowel sounds like its letter name (the letter i in fight). A short vowel sound does not (the letter i in fit).

11

Crossword

Sadness has a short a sound. Fear has an r-controlled e sound.

Complete the crossword. Use your knowledge of vowel sounds. Some letters have been placed for you.

S A D
C O A T
S L I P
B
L U N C H C
U E H
R E D T R A I N
L
D

Across
1. a feeling with a short a sound
2. clothing with a long a sound
3. fall on ice with a short i sound
5. a meal with a short u sound
7. a colour with a short e sound
8. choo-choo vehicle with a long a sound

Down
1. opposite of go with a short o sound
3. a round shape with an r-controlled e sound
4. a colour with a long u sound
6. a young person with a long i sound

12

100   *Sample answers provided.

Word Search

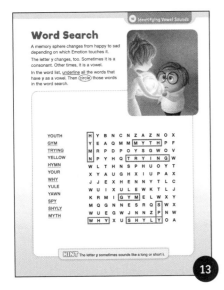

A memory sphere changes from happy to sad depending on which Emotion touches it.

The letter y changes, too. Sometimes it is a consonant. Other times, it is a vowel.

In the word list, underline all the words that have a y as a vowel. Then circle those words in the word search.

YOUTH	H	Y	B	N	C	N	Z	A	Z	N	O	X
GYM	Y	E	A	Q	M	M	M	Y	T	H	P	F
TRYING	M	R	P	D	P	O	Y	S	G	W	O	V
YELLOW	N	P	Y	H	Q	T	R	Y	I	N	G	W
HYMN	W	L	T	H	N	S	P	H	U	O	Y	T
YOUR	X	Y	A	U	G	H	X	I	U	P	A	X
WHY	J	J	E	X	H	E	N	N	Y	T	L	C
YULE	W	U	I	X	U	L	E	W	K	T	L	J
YAWN	K	R	M	I	G	Y	M	E	L	W	X	Y
SPY	M	Q	G	N	N	E	S	R	Q	S	W	X
SHYLY	W	U	E	G	W	J	N	N	Z	P	N	W
MYTH	W	H	Y	X	U	S	H	Y	L	Y	O	A

HINT The letter y sometimes sounds like a long or short i.

13

Unscramble the Words

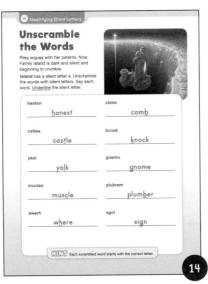

Riley argues with her parents. Now, Family Island is dark and silent and beginning to crumble.

Island has a silent letter s. Unscramble the words with silent letters. Say each word. Underline the silent letter.

heston
__honest__

cbmo
__comb__

cstlea
__castle__

kcnok
__knock__

ykol
__yolk__

gnemo
__gnome__

mucles
__muscle__

plubrem
__plumber__

weerh
__where__

sgni
__sign__

HINT Each scrambled word starts with the correct letter.

14

Fill In the Blanks

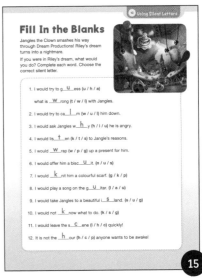

Jangles the Clown smashes his way through Dream Productions! Riley's dream turns into a nightmare.

If you were in Riley's dream, what would you do? Complete each word. Choose the correct silent letter.

1. I would try to g__u__ess (u / h / a) what is __w__rong (t / w / l) with Jangles.

2. I would try to ca__l__m (w / u / l) him down.

3. I would ask Jangles w__h__y (h / i / u) he is angry.

4. I would lis__t__en (k / t / s) to Jangle's reasons.

5. I would __w__rap (w / p / g) up a present for him.

6. I would offer him a bisc__u__it. (n / u / s)

7. I would __k__nit him a colourful scarf. (g / k / p)

8. I would play a song on the g__u__itar. (l / a / u)

9. I would take Jangles to a beautiful i__s__land. (s / u / g)

10. I would not __k__now what to do. (k / s / g)

11. I would leave the s__c__ene (l / h / c) quickly!

12. It is not the __h__our (h / c / p) anyone wants to be awake!

15

Crack the Code

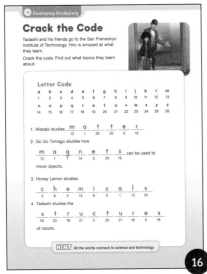

Tadashi and his friends go to the San Fransokyo Institute of Technology. Hiro is amazed at what they learn.

Crack the code. Find out what topics they learn about.

Letter Code

a	b	c	d	e	f	g	h	i	j	k	l	m
1	2	3	4	5	6	7	8	9	10	11	12	13

n	o	p	q	r	s	t	u	v	w	x	y	z
14	15	16	17	18	19	20	21	22	23	24	25	26

1. Wasabi studies __m a t t e r__
            13 1 20 20 5 18

2. Go Go Tomago studies how __m a g n e t s__ can be used to
        13 1 7 14 5 20 19
move objects.

3. Honey Lemon studies __c h e m i c a l s__
        3 8 5 13 9 3 1 12 19

4. Tadashi studies the __s t r u c t u r e s__
        19 20 18 21 3 20 21 18 5 19
of robots.

HINT All the words connect to science and technology.

16

Word Blocks

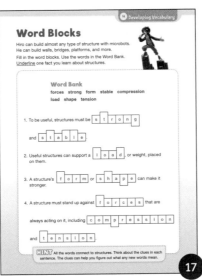

Hiro can build almost any type of structure with microbots. He can build walls, bridges, platforms, and more.

Fill in the word blocks. Use the words in the Word Bank. Underline one fact you learn about structures.

Word Bank
forces strong form stable compression
load shape tension

1. To be useful, structures must be s t r o n g and s t a b l e.

2. Useful structures can support a l o a d, or weight, placed on them.

3. A structure's f o r m or s h a p e can make it stronger.

4. A structure must stand up against f o r c e s that are always acting on it, including c o m p r e s s i o n and t e n s i o n.

HINT All the words connect to structures. Think about the clues in each sentence. The clues can help you figure out what any new words mean.

17

Unscramble the Words

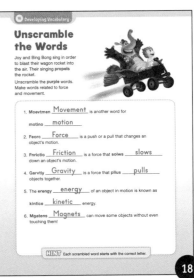

Joy and Bing Bong sing in order to blast their wagon rocket into the air. Their singing propels the rocket.

Unscramble the purple words. Make words related to force and movement.

1. Moevtmen __Movement__ is another word for motino __motion__.

2. Feorc __Force__ is a push or a pull that changes an object's motion.

3. Fnrictio __Friction__ is a force that solws __slows__ down an object's motion.

4. Garvtiy __Gravity__ is a force that pllus __pulls__ objects together.

5. The erengy __energy__ of an object in motion is known as kintice __kinetic__ energy.

6. Mgatens __Magnets__ can move some objects without even touching them!

HINT Each scrambled word starts with the correct letter.

18

Maze

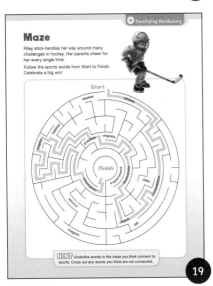

Riley stick-handles her way around many challenges in hockey. Her parents cheer for her every single time.

Follow the sports words from Start to Finish. Celebrate a big win!

HINT Underline words in the maze you think connect to sports. Cross out any words you think are not connected.

19

Solve the Riddles

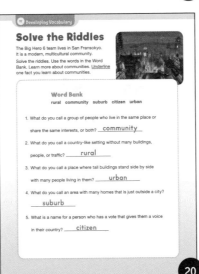

The Big Hero 6 team lives in San Fransokyo. It is a modern, multicultural community.

Solve the riddles. Use the words in the Word Bank. Learn more about communities. Underline one fact you learn about communities.

Word Bank
rural community suburb citizen urban

1. What do you call a group of people who live in the same place or share the same interests, or both? __community__

2. What do you call a country-like setting without many buildings, people, or traffic? __rural__

3. What do you call a place where tall buildings stand side by side with many people living in them? __urban__

4. What do you call an area with many homes that is just outside a city? __suburb__

5. What is a name for a person who has a vote that gives them a voice in their country? __citizen__

20

Crossword

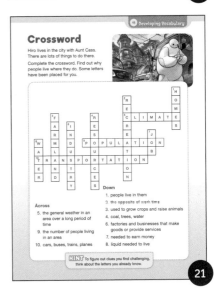

Hiro lives in the city with Aunt Cass. There are lots of things to do there.

Complete the crossword. Find out why people live where they do. Some letters have been placed for you.

Across
5. the general weather in an area over a long period of time
9. the number of people living in an area
10. cars, buses, trains, planes

Down
1. people live in them
2. the opposite of work time
3. used to grow crops and raise animals
4. coal, trees, water
6. factories and businesses that make goods or provide services
7. needed to earn money
8. liquid needed to live

HINT To figure out clues you find challenging, think about the letters you already know.

21

---

*Sample answers provided.

Answers

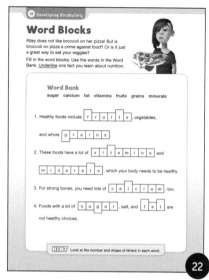

Word Blocks

Riley does not like broccoli on her pizza! But is broccoli on pizza a crime against food? Or is it just a great way to eat your veggies?

Fill in the word blocks. Use the words in the Word Bank. Underline one fact you learn about nutrition.

Word Bank

sugar calcium fat vitamins fruits grains minerals

1. Healthy foods include f r u i t s , vegetables,

   and whole g r a i n s .

2. These foods have a lot of v i t a m i n s and

   m i n e r a l s , which your body needs to be healthy.

3. For strong bones, you need lots of c a l c i u m , too.

4. Foods with a lot of s u g a r , salt, and f a t are

   not healthy choices.

HINT Look at the number and shape of letters in each word.

22

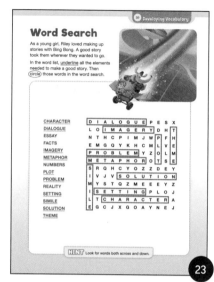

Word Search

As a young girl, Riley loved making up stories with Bing Bong. A good story took them wherever they wanted to go.

In the word list, underline all the elements needed to make a good story. Then circle those words in the word search.

CHARACTER
DIALOGUE
ESSAY
FACTS
IMAGERY
METAPHOR
NUMBERS
PLOT
PROBLEM
REALITY
SETTING
SIMILE
SOLUTION
THEME

```
D I A L O G U E P E S X
L O I M A G E R Y D H T
N T H C P I M J W P F H
E M G Q Y K H C M L V E
P R O B L E M Y Z O L M
M E T A P H O R O T S E
S R Q H C Y O Z Z D E Y
I V J V S O L U T I O N
M Y S T Q Z M E E E Y Z
I S E T T I N G P L O J
L T C H A R A C T E R A
E G C J X G O A Y N E J
```

HINT Look for words both across and down.

23

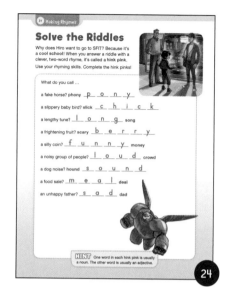

Solve the Riddles

Why does Hiro want to go to SFIT? Because it's a cool school! When you answer a riddle with a clever, two-word rhyme, it's called a hink pink. Use your rhyming skills. Complete the hink pinks!

What do you call ...

a fake horse? phony p o n y

a slippery baby bird? slick c h i c k

a lengthy tune? l o n g song

a frightening fruit? scary b e r r y

a silly coin? f u n n y money

a noisy group of people? l o u d crowd

a dog noise? hound s o u n d

a food sale? m e a l deal

an unhappy father? s a d dad

HINT One word in each hink pink is usually a noun. The other word is usually an adjective.

24

Solve the Rebus

Baymax is trying to figure out what is wrong with Hiro. But he is missing some important pieces of information.

The rhyming poem is missing pieces, too. Use the picture clues to figure out what they are.

Baymax is a healing bot,

But Hiro's hurt is not what he _thought_

Hiro has a broken ♥ _heart_

And helping it heal is Baymax's part.

Hiro's pain can't be healed in one 🌙 _night_

It'll take some time for him to feel all right.

First aid won't mend or heal his ━━ _break_

Friendship and love is what it will take.

HINT Sometimes the endings of rhyming words are spelled the same way (day, may) and sometimes they are not (day, weigh).

25

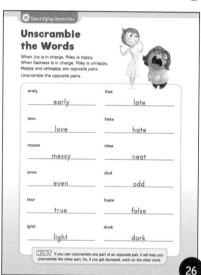

Unscramble the Words

When Joy is in charge, Riley is happy. When Sadness is in charge, Riley is unhappy. Happy and unhappy are opposite pairs. Unscramble the opposite pairs.

eraly	ltae
early	late
levo	heta
love	hate
myess	ntea
messy	neat
evne	dod
even	odd
teur	fsale
true	false
lghti	drak
light	dark

HINT If you can unscramble one part of an opposite pair, it will help you unscramble the other part. So, if you get stumped, work on the other word.

26

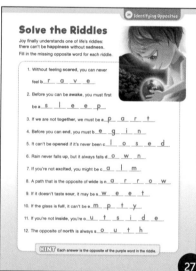

Solve the Riddles

Joy finally understands one of life's riddles: there can't be happiness without sadness.

Fill in the missing opposite word for each riddle.

1. Without feeling scared, you can never feel b r a v e

2. Before you can be awake, you must first be a s l e e p

3. If we are not together, we must be a p a r t

4. Before you can end, you must b e g i n

5. It can't be opened if it's never been c l o s e d

6. Rain never falls up, but it always falls d o w n

7. If you're not excited, you might be c a l m

8. A path that is the opposite of wide is n a r r o w

9. If it doesn't taste sour, it may be s w e e t

10. If the glass is full, it can't be e m p t y

11. If you're not inside, you're o u t s i d e

12. The opposite of north is always s o u t h

HINT Each answer is the opposite of the purple word in the riddle.

27

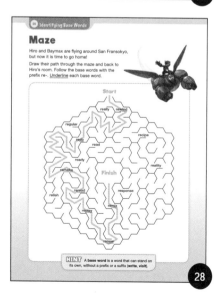

Maze

Hiro and Baymax are flying around San Fransokyo, but now it is time to go home!

Draw their path through the maze and back to Hiro's room. Follow the base words with the prefix re-. Underline each base word.

Start

Finish

HINT A base word is a word that can stand on its own, without a prefix or a suffix (write, visit).

28

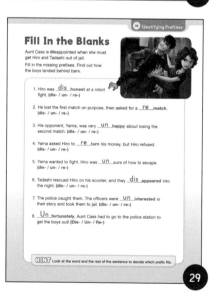

Fill In the Blanks

Aunt Cass is disappointed when she must get Hiro and Tadashi out of jail.

Fill in the missing prefixes. Find out how the boys landed behind bars.

1. Hiro was d i s honest at a robot fight. (dis- / un- / re-)

2. He lost the first match on purpose, then asked for a r e match. (dis- / un- / re-)

3. His opponent, Yama, was very u n happy about losing the second match. (dis- / un- / re-)

4. Yama asked Hiro to r e turn his money, but Hiro refused. (dis- / un- / re-)

5. Yama wanted to fight. Hiro was u n sure of how to escape. (dis- / un- / re-)

6. Tadashi rescued Hiro on his scooter, and they d i s appeared into the night. (dis- / un- / re-)

7. The police caught them. The officers were u n interested in their story and took them to jail. (dis- / un- / re-)

8. U n fortunately, Aunt Cass had to go to the police station to get the boys out! (Dis- / Un- / Re-)

HINT Look at the word and the rest of the sentence to decide which prefix fits.

29

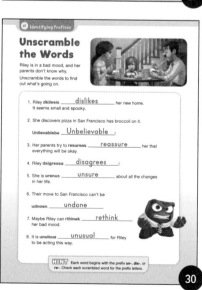

Unscramble the Words

Riley is in a bad mood, and her parents don't know why.

Unscramble the words to find out what's going on.

1. Riley dkilesis _dislikes_ her new home. It seems small and spooky.

2. She discovers pizza in San Francisco has broccoli on it. Unlievablebe _Unbelievable_ .

3. Her parents try to resureas _reassure_ her that everything will be okay.

4. Riley dsigreesa _disagrees_ .

5. She is urenus _unsure_ about all the changes in her life.

6. Their move to San Francisco can't be undnoen _undone_ .

7. Maybe Riley can rthienk _rethink_ her bad mood.

8. It is unulsua _unusual_ for Riley to be acting this way.

HINT Each word begins with the prefix un-, dis-, or re-. Check each scrambled word for the prefix letters.

30

*Sample answers provided.

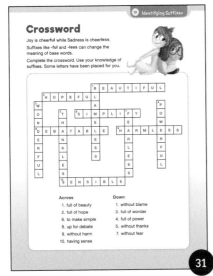

Crossword

Joy is cheerful while Sadness is cheerless.

Suffixes like -ful and -less can change the meaning of base words.

Complete the crossword. Use your knowledge of suffixes. Some letters have been placed for you.

Crossword answers:
- BEAUTIFUL
- HOPEFUL
- SIMPLIFY
- DEBATABLE
- HARMLESS
- SENSIBLE

Across
1. full of beauty
2. full of hope
6. to make simple
8. up for debate
9. without harm
10. having sense

Down
1. without blame
3. full of wonder
4. full of power
5. without thanks
7. without fear

31

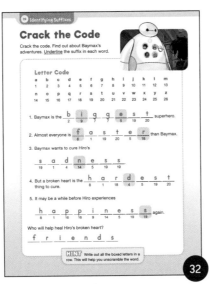

Crack the Code

Crack the code. Find out about Baymax's adventures. Underline the suffix in each word.

Letter Code

a	b	c	d	e	f	g	h	i	j	k	l	m
1	2	3	4	5	6	7	8	9	10	11	12	13

n	o	p	q	r	s	t	u	v	w	x	y	z
14	15	16	17	18	19	20	21	22	23	24	25	26

1. Baymax is the **b i g g e s t** superhero.
   2   9   7   7   5   19   20

2. Almost everyone is **f a s t e r** than Baymax.
   6   1   19   20   5   18

3. Baymax wants to cure Hiro's
   s a d n e s s
   19   1   4   14   5   19   19

4. But a broken heart is the **h a r d e s t**
   8   1   18   4   5   19   20
   thing to cure.

5. It may be a while before Hiro experiences
   h a p p i n e s s again.
   8   1   16   16   9   14   5   19   19

Who will help heal Hiro's broken heart?

f r i e n d s

HINT Write out all the boxed letters in a row. This will help you unscramble the word.

32

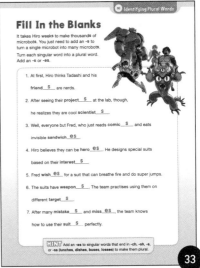

Fill In the Blanks

It takes Hiro weeks to make thousands of microbots. You just need to add an -s to turn a single microbot into many microbots.

Turn each singular word into a plural word. Add an -s or -es.

1. At first, Hiro thinks Tadashi and his friend **s** are nerds.

2. After seeing their project **s** at the lab, though, he realizes they are cool scientist **s**.

3. Well, everyone but Fred, who just reads comic **s** and eats invisible sandwich **es**.

4. Hiro believes they can be hero **es**. He designs special suits based on their interest **s**.

5. Fred wish **es** for a suit that can breathe fire and do super jumps.

6. The suits have weapon **s**. The team practises using them on different target **s**.

7. After many mistake **s** and miss **es**, the team knows how to use their suit **s** perfectly.

HINT Add an -es to singular words that end in -ch, -sh, -s, or -ss (lunches, dishes, buses, losses) to make them plural.

33

Maze

Joy and Sadness are lost in Long Term Memory. They need to get back to Headquarters fast.

Draw their path through the maze back to Headquarters. Follow the correctly spelled plurals.

Start — feet, days, dayes, foots, stories, storys, mouses, halves, mics, halfs, sheep, sheeps, dreams, dreamz, candys, candles — Finish

HINT Not all words become plural by adding an -s or -es. And sometimes, when a word ends in a consonant y, the y becomes an i and -es is added.

34

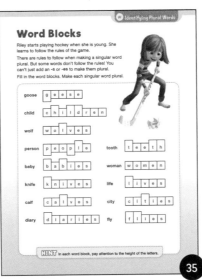

Word Blocks

Riley starts playing hockey when she is young. She learns to follow the rules of the game.

There are rules to follow when making a singular word plural. But some words don't follow the rules! You can't just add an -s or -es to make them plural. Fill in the word blocks. Make each singular word plural.

goose	g e e s e		
child	c h i l d r e n		
wolf	w o l v e s		
person	p e o p l e	tooth	t e e t h
baby	b a b i e s	woman	w o m e n
knife	k n i v e s	life	l i v e s
calf	c a l v e s	city	c i t i e s
diary	d i a r i e s	fly	f l i e s

HINT In each word block, pay attention to the height of the letters.

35

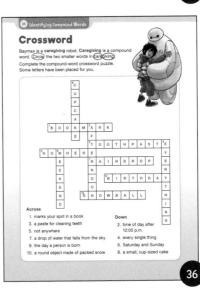

Crossword

Baymax is a caregiving robot. Caregiving is a compound word. Circle the two smaller words in caregiving.

Complete the compound-word crossword puzzle. Some letters have been placed for you.

Crossword answers:
- BOOKMARK
- TOOTHPASTE
- NOWHERE
- RAINDROP
- BIRTHDAY
- SNOWBALL

Across
1. marks your spot in a book
3. a paste for cleaning teeth
5. not anywhere
7. a drop of water that falls from the sky
9. the day a person is born
10. a round object made of packed snow

Down
2. time of day after 12:00 p.m.
4. every single thing
6. Saturday and Sunday
8. a small, cup-sized cake

36

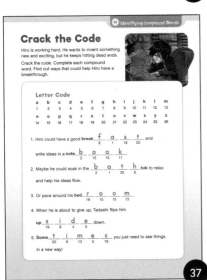

Crack the Code

Hiro is working hard. He wants to invent something new and exciting, but he keeps hitting dead ends.

Crack the code. Complete each compound word. Find out ways that could help Hiro have a breakthrough.

Letter Code

a	b	c	d	e	f	g	h	i	j	k	l	m
1	2	3	4	5	6	7	8	9	10	11	12	13

n	o	p	q	r	s	t	u	v	w	x	y	z
14	15	16	17	18	19	20	21	22	23	24	25	26

1. Hiro could have a good break **f a s t** and
   6   1   19   20
   write ideas in a note **b o o k**.
   2   15   15   11

2. Maybe he could soak in the **b a t h** tub to relax
   2   1   20   8
   and help his ideas flow.

3. Or pace around his bed **r o o m**.
   18   15   15   13

4. When he is about to give up, Tadashi flips him
   up **s i d e** down.
   19   9   4   5

5. Some **t i m e s** you just need to see things
   20   9   13   5   19
   in a new way!

37

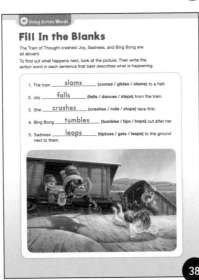

Fill In the Blanks

The Train of Thought crashes! Joy, Sadness, and Bing Bong are all aboard.

To find out what happens next, look at the picture. Then write the action word in each sentence that best describes what is happening.

1. The train **slams** (comes / glides / slams) to a halt.
2. Joy **falls** (falls / dances / steps) from the train.
3. She **crashes** (crashes / rolls / stops) face first.
4. Bing Bong **tumbles** (tumbles / tips / hops) out after her.
5. Sadness **leaps** (tiptoes / gets / leaps) to the ground next to them.

38

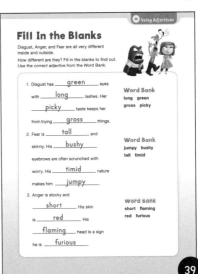

Fill In the Blanks

Disgust, Anger, and Fear are all very different inside and outside.

How different are they? Fill in the blanks to find out. Use the correct adjective from the Word Bank.

1. Disgust has **green** eyes with **long** lashes. Her **picky** taste keeps her from trying **gross** things.

   Word Bank
   long   green
   gross   picky

2. Fear is **tall** and skinny. His **bushy** eyebrows are often scrunched with worry. His **timid** nature makes him **jumpy**.

   Word Bank
   jumpy   bushy
   tall   timid

3. Anger is stocky and **short**. His skin is **red**. His **flaming** head is a sign he is **furious**.

   Word Bank
   short   flaming
   red   furious

39

*Sample answers provided.

103

Answers

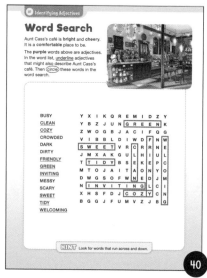

Word Search

Aunt Cass's café is **bright** and **cheery**. It is a **comfortable** place to be.
The **purple** words above are adjectives. In the word list, underline adjectives that might also describe Aunt Cass's café. Then circle these words in the word search.

BUSY
CLEAN
COZY
CROWDED
DARK
DIRTY
FRIENDLY
GREEN
INVITING
MESSY
SCARY
SWEET
TIDY
WELCOMING

```
Y X I K Q R E M I D Z Y
Y B Z J U N G R E E N K
Z W O G B J A C I F Q G
V I B B L D I W D F N W
S W E E T V R C R R N E
J M X A K G U L H I U L
T T I D Y B S E K E P C
M T O J A I T A O N Y O
D W G S O F W N E D J M
N I N V I T I N G L C I
X H S F D J C O Z Y C N G
B G G J F U M V Z J B G
```

HINT Look for words that run across and down.

40

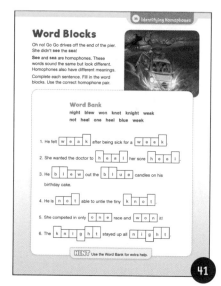

Word Blocks

Oh no! Go Go drives off the end of the pier. She didn't **see** the sea!
See and **sea** are homophones. These words sound the same but look different. Homophones also have different meanings.
Complete each sentence. Fill in the word blocks. Use the correct homophone pair.

Word Bank
night blew won knot knight weak
not heal one heel blue week

1. He felt `weak` after being sick for a `week`.
2. She wanted the doctor to `heal` her sore `heel`.
3. He `blew` out the `blue` candles on his birthday cake.
4. He is `not` able to untie the tiny `knot`.
5. She competed in only `one` race and `won` it!
6. The `knight` stayed up all `night`.

HINT Use the Word Bank for extra help.

41

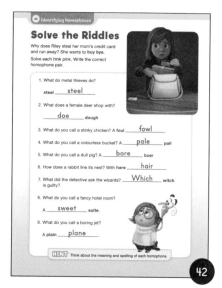

Solve the Riddles

Why does Riley steal her mom's credit card and run away? She wants to **buy bye**.
Solve each hink pink. Write the correct homophone pair.

1. What do metal thieves do?
   steal `steel`
2. What does a female deer shop with?
   `doe` dough
3. What do you call a stinky chicken? A foul `fowl`
4. What do you call a colourless bucket? A `pale` pail
5. What do you call a dull pig? A `bore` boar
6. How does a rabbit line its nest? With hare `hair`
7. What did the detective ask the wizards? `Which` witch is guilty?
8. What do you call a fancy hotel room?
   A `sweet` suite.
9. What do you call a boring jet?
   A plain `plane`

HINT Think about the meaning and spelling of each homophone.

42

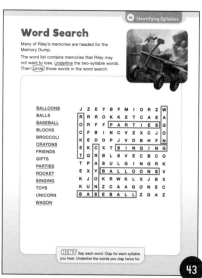

Word Search

Many of Riley's memories are headed for the Memory Dump.
The word list contains memories that Riley may not want to lose. Underline the two-syllable words. Then circle those words in the word search.

BALLOONS
BALLS
BASEBALL
BLOCKS
BROCCOLI
CRAYONS
FRIENDS
GIFTS
PARTIES
ROCKET
SINGING
TOYS
UNICORN
WAGON

```
J Z E Y B F M I O R Z W
R R O K K E T C A E A A
O R F F P A R T I E S G
C F B I N C V Z X C J O
K E D D P J V D B H F N
E K C X T S I N G I N G
I Q R B L S V E C B C O
T P A S U L G I N G R K
E X Y B A L L O O N S V
K J O K R W K L X J B X
K U N Z C A A G O N E C
B A S E B A L L Z G A Z
```

HINT Say each word. Clap for each syllable you hear. Underline the words you clap twice for.

43

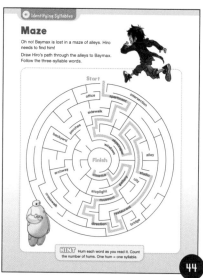

Maze

Oh no! Baymax is lost in a maze of alleys. Hiro needs to find him!
Draw Hiro's path through the alleys to Baymax. Follow the three-syllable words.

HINT Hum each word as you read it. Count the number of hums. One hum = one syllable.

44

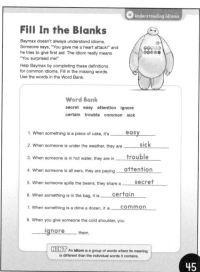

Fill In the Blanks

Baymax doesn't always understand idioms. Someone says, "You gave me a heart attack!" and he tries to give first aid. The idiom really means "You surprised me!"
Help Baymax by completing these definitions for common idioms. Fill in the missing words. Use the words in the Word Bank.

Word Bank
secret easy attention ignore
certain trouble common sick

1. When something is a piece of cake, it's `easy`
2. When someone is under the weather, they are `sick`
3. When someone is in hot water, they are in `trouble`
4. When someone is all ears, they are paying `attention`
5. When someone spills the beans, they share a `secret`
6. When something is in the bag, it is `certain`
7. When something is a dime a dozen, it is `common`
8. When you give someone the cold shoulder, you `ignore` them.

HINT An **idiom** is a group of words where its meaning is different than the individual words it contains.

45

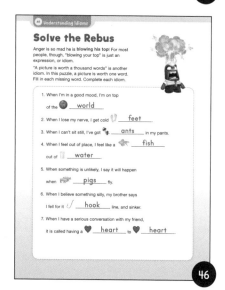

Solve the Rebus

Anger is so mad he is "blowing his top"! For most people, though, "blowing your top" is just an expression, or idiom.
"A picture is worth a thousand words" is another idiom. In this puzzle, a picture is worth one word. Fill in each missing word. Complete each idiom.

1. When I'm in a good mood, I'm on top of the 🌍 `world`
2. When I lose my nerve, I get cold 🦶 `feet`
3. When I can't sit still, I've got 🐜 `ants` in my pants.
4. When I feel out of place, I feel like a 🐟 `fish` out of 💧 `water`
5. When something is unlikely, I say it will happen when 🐷 `pigs` fly.
6. When I believe something silly, my brother says I fell for it 🪝 `hook` line, and sinker.
7. When I have a serious conversation with my friend, it is called having a ❤️ `heart` to ❤️ `heart`

46

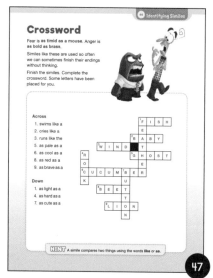

Crossword

Fear is as **timid as a mouse**. Anger is as **bold as brass**.
Similes like these are used so often we can sometimes finish their endings without thinking.
Finish the similes. Complete the crossword. Some letters have been placed for you.

Across
1. swims like a
2. cries like a
3. runs like the
5. as pale as a
6. as cool as a
8. as red as a
9. as brave as a

Down
1. as light as a
4. as hard as a
7. as cute as a

```
        F I S H
        E
       B A B Y
        T
  W I N D
        G H O S T
 R      O
 O      O
 C U C U M B E R
 K      E
     B E E T
        T
     L I O N
        N
```

HINT A simile compares two things using the words **like** or **as**.

47

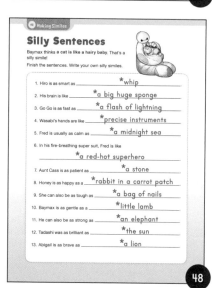

Silly Sentences

Baymax thinks a cat is like a hairy baby. That's a silly simile!
Finish the sentences. Write your own silly similes.

1. Hiro is as smart as `*whip`
2. His brain is like `*a big huge sponge`
3. Go Go is as fast as `*a flash of lightning`
4. Wasabi's hands are like `*precise instruments`
5. Fred is usually as calm as `*a midnight sea`
6. In his fire-breathing super suit, Fred is like `*a red-hot superhero`
7. Aunt Cass is as patient as `*a stone`
8. Honey is as happy as a `*rabbit in a carrot patch`
9. She can also be as tough as `*a bag of nails`
10. Baymax is as gentle as a `*little lamb`
11. He can also be as strong as `*an elephant`
12. Tadashi was as brilliant as `*the sun`
13. Abigail is as brave as `*a lion`

48

*Sample answers provided.

Word Blocks

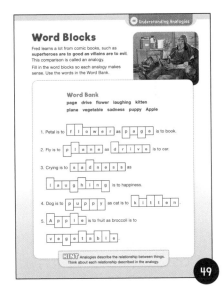

Understanding Analogies

Fred learns a lot from comic books, such as **superheroes are to good as villains are to evil.** This comparison is called an analogy.

Fill in the word blocks so each analogy makes sense. Use the words in the Word Bank.

Word Bank
page drive flower laughing kitten
plane vegetable sadness puppy Apple

1. Petal is to `f l o w e r` as `p a g e` is to book.

2. Fly is to `p l a n e` as `d r i v e` is to car.

3. Crying is to `s a d n e s s` as
   `l a u g h i n g` is to happiness.

4. Dog is to `p u p p y` as cat is to `k i t t e n`.

5. `A p p l e` is to fruit as broccoli is to
   `v e g e t a b l e`.

HINT Analogies describe the relationship between things. Think about each relationship described in the analogy.

49

Fill In the Blanks

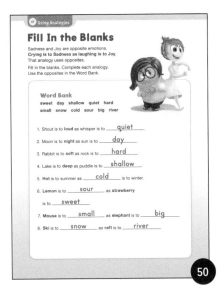

Using Analogies

Sadness and Joy are opposite emotions. **Crying is to Sadness as laughing is to Joy.** That analogy uses opposites.

Fill in the blanks. Complete each analogy. Use the opposites in the Word Bank.

Word Bank
sweet day shallow quiet hard
small snow cold sour big river

1. Shout is to **loud** as whisper is to ___quiet___

2. Moon is to **night** as sun is to ___day___

3. Rabbit is to **soft** as rock is to ___hard___

4. Lake is to **deep** as puddle is to ___shallow___

5. Hot is to **summer** as ___cold___ is to winter.

6. Lemon is to ___sour___ as strawberry
   is to ___sweet___

7. Mouse is to ___small___ as elephant is to ___big___

8. Ski is to ___snow___ as raft is to ___river___

50

Silly Sentences

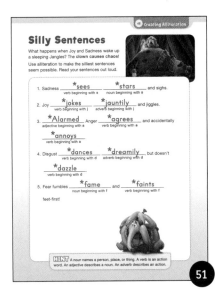

Creating Alliteration

What happens when Joy and Sadness wake up a sleeping Jangles? The **clown** causes chaos!

Use alliteration to make the silliest sentences seem possible. Read your sentences out loud.

1. Sadness _*sees_ _*stars_ and sighs.
   verb beginning with s   noun beginning with s

2. Joy _*jokes_ _*jauntily_ and jiggles.
   verb beginning with j   adverb beginning with j

3. _*Alarmed_ Anger _*agrees_ and accidentally
   adjective beginning with a   verb beginning with a
   *annoys
   verb beginning with a

4. Disgust _*dances_ _*dreamily_ but doesn't
   verb beginning with d   adverb beginning with d
   *dazzle
   verb beginning with d

5. Fear fumbles _*fame_ and _*faints_
   noun beginning with f   verb beginning with f
   feet-first!

HINT A noun names a person, place, or thing. A verb is an action word. An adjective describes a noun. An adverb describes an action.

51

Solve the Riddles

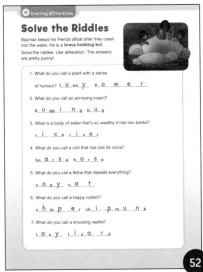

Creating Alliteration

Baymax keeps his friends afloat after they crash into the water. He is a **brave** bobbing bot.

Solve the riddles. Use alliteration. The answers are pretty punny!

1. What do you call a plant with a sense
   of humour? `f u n n y  n o w e r`

2. What do you call an annoying insect?
   `b u g g i n g  b u g`

3. What is a body of water that's so wealthy it has two banks?
   `r i c h  r i v e r`

4. What do you call a colt that has lost its voice?
   ho`a r s e  h o r s e`

5. What do you call a feline that repeats everything?
   `c o p y  c a t`

6. What do you call a happy rodent?
   c`h i p p e r  ch i p m u n k`

7. What do you call a snoozing reptile?
   `l a z y  l i z a r` d

52

Crossword

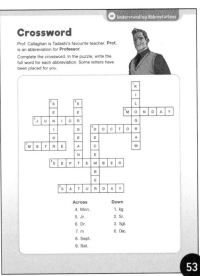

Understanding Abbreviations

Prof. Callaghan is Tadashi's favourite teacher. **Prof.** is an abbreviation for **Professor.**

Complete the crossword. In the puzzle, write the full word for each abbreviation. Some letters have been placed for you.

Across
4. Mon.
5. Jr.
6. Dr.
7. m
8. Sept.
9. Sat.

Down
1. kg
2. Sr.
3. Sgt.
6. Dec.

53

Unscramble the Words

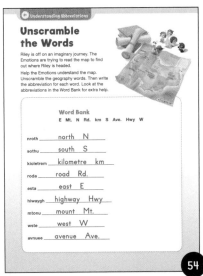

Understanding Abbreviations

Riley is off on an imaginary journey. The Emotions are trying to read the map to find out where Riley is headed.

Help the Emotions understand the map. Unscramble the geography words. Then write the abbreviation for each word. Look at the abbreviations in the Word Bank for extra help.

Word Bank
E Mt. N Rd. km S Ave. Hwy W

nroth	north	N
sothu	south	S
kioletrem	kilometre	km
roda	road	Rd.
esta	east	E
hiwaygh	highway	Hwy
mtonu	mount	Mt.
wste	west	W
avnuee	avenue	Ave.

54

Word Search

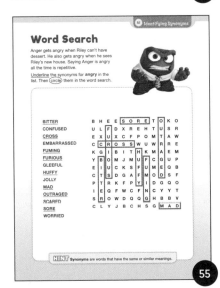

Identifying Synonyms

Anger gets angry when Riley can't have dessert. He also gets angry when he sees Riley's new house. Saying Anger is angry all the time is repetitive.

Underline the synonyms for **angry** in the list. Then (circle) them in the word search.

BITTER
CONFUSED
CROSS
EMBARRASSED
FUMING
FURIOUS
GLEEFUL
HUFFY
JOLLY
MAD
OUTRAGED
SCARED
SORE
WORRIED

```
B H E E S O R E T O K O
U L F D X R E H T U S R
E X U X C F P O M T A W
I C R O S S W U W R R E
K G I B I T H K M A E M
Y B O M J M U F C G U P
E I U C K S F U M E Q B
C T S D G A F M O D S F
P T R K F P Y I D G Q O
I E Q F W C F N C Y Y T
S R O W D Q Q G H B B V
C L Y J B C H S G M A D
```

HINT Synonyms are words that have the same or similar meanings.

55

Crossword

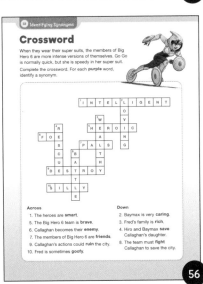

Identifying Synonyms

When they wear their super suits, the members of Big Hero 6 are more intense versions of themselves. Go Go is normally quick, but she is speedy in her super suit.

Complete the crossword. For each **purple** word, identify a synonym.

Across
1. The heroes are **smart.**
5. The Big Hero 6 team is **brave.**
6. Callaghan becomes their **enemy.**
7. The members of Big Hero 6 are **friends.**
9. Callaghan's actions could **ruin** the city.
10. Fred is sometimes **goofy.**

Down
2. Baymax is very **caring.**
3. Fred's family is **rich.**
4. Hiro and Baymax **save** Callaghan's daughter.
8. The team must **fight** Callaghan to save the city.

56

Word Blocks

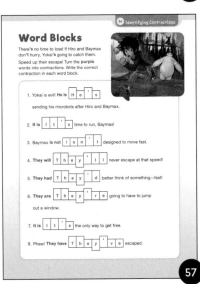

Identifying Contractions

There's no time to lose! If Hiro and Baymax don't hurry, Yokai's going to catch them.

Speed up their escape! Turn the **purple** words into contractions. Write the correct contraction in each word block.

1. Yokai is evil! He is `H e ' s`
   sending his microbots after Hiro and Baymax.

2. It is `I t ' s` time to run, Baymax!

3. Baymax is not `i s n ' t` designed to move fast.

4. They will `T h e y ' l l` never escape at that speed!

5. They had `T h e y ' d` better think of something—fast!

6. They are `T h e y ' r e` going to have to jump
   out a window.

7. It is `I t ' s` the only way to get free.

8. Phew! They have `T h e y ' v e` escaped.

57

---

*Sample answers provided.

105

Answers

Picture Search

Riley is unhappy in San Francisco. She plans to run away back to Minnesota, but she isn't sure she should.

Look at the pictures. Predict which picture shows the next part of the story. Circle your choice.

What helped you make your prediction?

*The third picture shows Riley leaving the bus. So I think she knows she made a mistake by running away. I think she decides to go home.

HINT Making predictions can help you think about the story and understand it.

58

Crack the Code

Bing Bong and Joy need to get back to Headquarters. They want to stop Riley from running away. But Bing Bong is stuck in the Memory Dump!

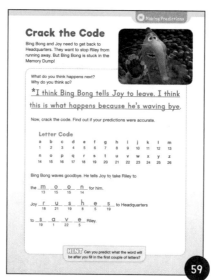

What do you think happens next? Why do you think so?

*I think Bing Bong tells Joy to leave. I think this is what happens because he's waving bye.

Now, crack the code. Find out if your predictions were accurate.

Letter Code

a	b	c	d	e	f	g	h	i	j	k	l	m
1	2	3	4	5	6	7	8	9	10	11	12	13

n	o	p	q	r	s	t	u	v	w	x	y	z
14	15	16	17	18	19	20	21	22	23	24	25	26

Bing Bong waves goodbye. He tells Joy to take Riley to

the m o o n for him.
    13 15 15 14

Joy r u s h e s to Headquarters
    18 21 19 8 5 19

to s a v e Riley.
   19 1 22 5

HINT Can you predict what the word will be after you fill in the first couple of letters?

59

Fill In the Blanks

Tadashi and Hiro have a close relationship. They know each other well.

Read the story to learn more about the brothers. Pay attention to the details so you can answer the questions on page 61.

Tadashi is worried about his little brother, Hiro. Hiro is smart, but he wastes his time on robot fights instead of going to school.

Tadashi wants to show Hiro there are better things to do. After a robot fight, he takes Hiro to the robotics lab at SFIT. Tadashi is a student there.

Hiro is amazed by the lab and all the cool subjects Tadashi is studying. Hiro feels inspired!

When they leave the lab, Hiro cannot stop talking about how much he wants to be accepted as a student at SFIT.

How does Tadashi feel about Hiro's robot-fighting? How do you know?

*Tadashi doesn't like it. He thinks Hiro is wasting his time on robot fights instead of going to school.

Where does Tadashi take Hiro? Why there?

*Tadashi takes Hiro to the robotics lab at SFIT. He wants to show Tadashi there are better things to do than robot fights.

HINT As you read, underline key details about the characters.

60

What does Hiro think of the lab at Tadashi's school?

*Hiro thinks the lab is amazing.

Do you think Tadashi is a good older brother? Why?

*I think Tadashi is a good older brother because he worries about Hiro. He wants Hiro to go to school and learn.

61

Out of Order

Read the story about Riley's move to San Francisco. Pay attention to the story events so you can retell the story in order on page 63.

When Riley's dad gets a new job in San Francisco, Riley's heart sinks. San Francisco is in California—far away from where they live in Minnesota.

Soon after, Riley's parents sell their home and pack up all their belongings. Next, they drive toward California. Riley is excited when she sees San Francisco's famous Golden Gate Bridge.

Her excitement vanishes later on when she sees where they will live. It is a small, dark home squished into a long row of other small, dark homes.

Riley misses her old friend Meg. Riley talks to Meg on her laptop, but Riley gets mad when Meg mentions a new friend. Riley slams her laptop shut.

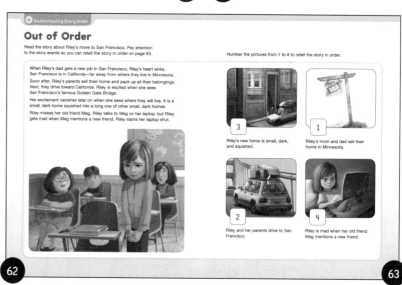

Number the pictures from 1 to 4 to retell the story in order.

3 — Riley's new home is small, dark, and squished.

1 — Riley's mom and dad sell their home in Minnesota.

2 — Riley and her parents drive to San Francisco.

4 — Riley is mad when her old friend Meg mentions a new friend.

62   **63**

Fill In the Blanks

Look at the picture. Read the story about the mystery man in the lab. Pay attention to information about the characters and events.

The Big Hero 6 team wants to catch the man in the mask. They follow him to an abandoned lab, where they find old videos from security cameras.

The videos show a group of people touring the lab. Some are wearing white lab coats while others wear military uniforms. One man wears an expensive suit. He's in charge.

The man boldly announces that history will be made. He orders the scientists to start two teleportation portals. They hesitate because it looks like there might be a problem with one of the portals. The man tells them to continue anyway.

Seconds later, disaster strikes. One portal explodes and the video screens go dark.

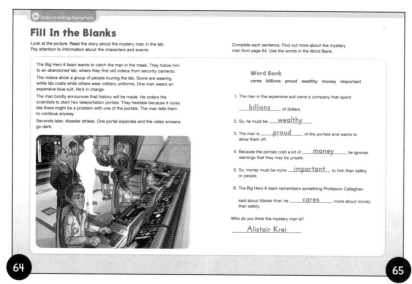

Complete each sentence. Find out more about the mystery man from page 64. Use the words in the Word Bank.

Word Bank
cares billions proud wealthy money important

1. The man in the expensive suit owns a company that spent
   billions of dollars.

2. So, he must be wealthy .

3. The man is proud of the portals and wants to show them off.

4. Because the portals cost a lot of money , he ignores warnings that they may be unsafe.

5. So, money must be more important to him than safety or people.

6. The Big Hero 6 team remembers something Professor Callaghan said about Alistair Krei: he cares more about money than safety.

Who do you think the mystery man is?

Alistair Krei

64   **65**

Crack the Code

Read the story about Riley and Bing Bong's trip. Then answer the questions on page 67.

Riley and Bing Bong want to take their band on tour. They decide to go to Australia. Riley has heard that many interesting animals live there.

They pack snacks for their trip and climb into their wagon rocket. They count down to launch: five … four … three … two … one!

Nothing happens.

Uh-oh. Why won't the rocket start? It needs fuel! Bing Bong says the rocket runs on song power, so they start singing as loudly as they can.

The rocket rolls forward and picks up speed. Riley and Bing Bong fly out the window and across the ocean toward Australia!

66

106   *Sample answers provided.

Page 67

Use information from the story on page 66 to answer the questions.

1. Where do Riley and Bing Bong go on tour?
A u s t r a l i a

2. What vehicle do they use to travel?
w a g o n r o c k e t

3. What do Riley and Bing Bong bring with them on their trip?
s n a c k s

4. What does the rocket need to start?
f u e l

5. What do they do to fuel the rocket?
s i n g

Unscramble the boxed letters to answer the question.
What animals will Riley and Bing Bong see in Australia?

Kangaroos, wallabies, and k o a l a s

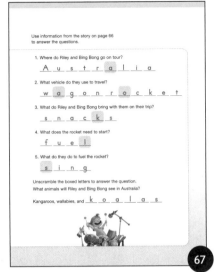

67

Page 68–69

Reading for Meaning

Solve the Rebus

Solve the Rebus. Write the correct words in the blank spaces.

Riley is __baby__ sitting a boy named Devan. They aren't getting along at first.

Devan wants a __cupcake__ but Riley says no. She's made them for her friend. The little boy stamps his __feet__.

Big __tears__ roll down his cheeks. Riley has an __idea__.

She remembers her __first__ time on __skates__. She kept falling. Her parents sat her __down__ on a bench. Her dad sprinkled __snowflakes__ on her head. With a __smile__, he called her a hothead.

He said she needed to cool __down__. That made her laugh and she tried skating again.

Riley tells Devan the __tale__. She pretends to sprinkle __snowflakes__ on his head. He laughs.

Devan is ready to play a __game__ with Riley.

The __pair__ of them have so much __fun__ playing together!

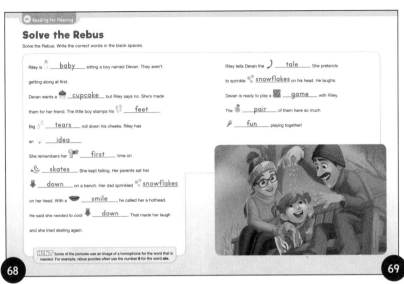

HINT Some of the pictures use an image of a homophone for the word that is needed. For example, rebus puzzles often use the number 8 for the word ate.

68 **69**

Page 70–71

Reading for Meaning

Crossword

Read the story about how Big Hero 6 became a superhero team.

Hiro makes amazing super suits for his friends.

Hiro makes Baymax a suit of armour with rocket thrusters so he can fly. He then makes Fred a fire-breathing, super-jumping monster suit. He makes laser gloves for Wasabi and a portable chemical factory for Honey Lemon's purse. For Go Go, Hiro makes super-fast running discs.

Hiro makes himself a suit with super-strong magnets. The magnets connect with Baymax's suit, so Hiro can hang on while they fly.

The team practises for hours in their suits. There are accidents. Honey Lemon covers the yard in chemical goo, Baymax shoots his rocket arm through a wall, and Fred sets the lawn on fire.

But eventually, the team is ready to fight Yokai. Big Hero 6 is born!

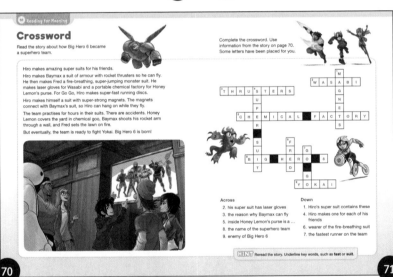

Complete the crossword. Use information from the story on page 70. Some letters have been placed for you.

THRUSTERS
WASABI
CHEMICAL FACTORY
BIG HERO
YOKAI

Across
2. his super suit has laser gloves
3. the reason why Baymax can fly
5. inside Honey Lemon's purse is a ...
8. the name of the superhero team
9. enemy of Big Hero 6

Down
1. Hiro's super suit contains these
4. Hiro makes one for each of his friends
6. wearer of the fire-breathing suit
7. the fastest runner on the team

HINT Reread the story. Underline key words, such as fast or suit.

70 **71**

Page 72

Reading for Meaning

Silly Sentences

An explosion destroys the Tech Showcase at SFIT. The blast blows out doors and windows. The sentences below are knocked around. Put the words back in order so the sentences make sense.

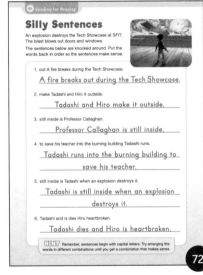

1. out A fire breaks during the Tech Showcase.
   A fire breaks out during the Tech Showcase.

2. make Tadashi and Hiro it outside.
   Tadashi and Hiro make it outside.

3. still inside Professor Callaghan.
   Professor Callaghan is still inside.

4. to save his teacher into the burning building Tadashi runs.
   Tadashi runs into the burning building to save his teacher.

5. still inside is Tadashi when an explosion destroys it.
   Tadashi is still inside when an explosion destroys it.

6. Tadashi and is dies Hiro heartbroken.
   Tadashi dies and Hiro is heartbroken.

HINT Remember, sentences begin with capital letters. Try arranging the words in different combinations until you get a combination that makes sense.

72

Page 73

Reading for Meaning

Fill In the Blanks

Hiro and Baymax have had a busy night! What have they been up to? Fill in the blanks. Look at the words before and after the blank space to figure out which word is missing. Use the words in the Word Bank for extra help.

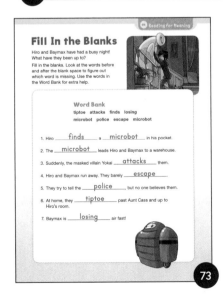

Word Bank
tiptoe   attacks   finds   losing
microbot   police   escape   microbot

1. Hiro __finds__ a __microbot__ in his pocket.

2. The __microbot__ leads Hiro and Baymax to a warehouse.

3. Suddenly, the masked villain Yokai __attacks__ them.

4. Hiro and Baymax run away. They barely __escape__.

5. They try to tell the __police__ but no one believes them.

6. At home, they __tiptoe__ past Aunt Cass and up to Hiro's room.

7. Baymax is __losing__ air fast!

73

Page 74

Using End Punctuation

Fill In the Blanks

The Emotions are at the control panel. Things are not going well! What is happening? Fill in the missing end punctuation to find out. Use the punctuation from the box.

Punctuation
? ! .

1. The Emotions are a mess. __or !__

2. They watch as Riley misses the puck at hockey tryouts. __.__

3. Why is this happening. __?__

4. Anger is so frustrated he wants to scream. __!__

5. Who can help Riley. __?__

6. She'll be so sad if she doesn't make the team. __or !__

7. What if they distract her. __?__

8. Then she can take a breath and calm down. __.__

9. Will their plan work. __?__

10. Can they do enough to help Riley succeed at tryouts. __?__

11. They need to try something. __or !__

12. What do you think happened. __?__

HINT Many questions begin with who, what, where, why, when, and how.

74

Page 75

Using Commas

What's Missing?

During hockey tryouts, Riley is angry, frustrated, and annoyed. She yells, throws her stick, and stomps off the ice.
If you were Riley's friend, what would you say to her? To get some ideas, fill in the missing commas.

Hi, Riley. Are you okay? I'm sorry that tryouts were so hard, frustrating, and difficult.

What do you think happened? Did you trip, fall, and lose your balance?

Maybe your skate laces ripped, broke, or came untied.

Sometimes people have terrible, horrible, bad days.

My worst day was when I was late for school, forgot my homework, and spilled red juice on my shirt.

It must be hard to move to a new city, leave your friends, and go to a new school.

Would it help if we talked about it, Riley? You can yell, shout, and cry!

Let's hang out! I will make sure to have snacks, drinks, and good music.

HINT Commas separate a series of words or ideas. They show pauses in sentences. Use commas when speaking to a person.

75

---

*Sample answers provided.

Answers

What's Missing?

Abigail Callaghan will be the first person to teleport. She might be saying, "This is amazing!"

Fill in the missing quotation marks. Find out what happens during Abigail's test run.

"Ready to go for a ride, Abigail?" asks Alistair Krei.

Abigail checks her seatbelt and controls in the pod one last time. She says, "We've invited all these people. Might as well give them a show."

Abigail flips a few switches and settles back against her seat. Then, a technician spots a problem.

The General asks, "Mr. Krei, is there a problem?"

Krei replies, "No. No problem. It's well within the parameters. Let's move forward."

The countdown begins. The cabin pressure is a go and the pod is engaged.

The technician shouts, "Field breach!"

They lose all contact with the pod. The pilot is gone.

HINT Use quotation marks before and after someone speaks.

76

Silly Sentences

Abigail is lost and alone in the portal. Will she be trapped forever?

Imagine you were in the portal with Abigail. What would you be thinking? Finish the sentences. Use the punctuation from the box.

Punctuation
. , ? " "

What *are we going to do now?
No one will ever find us.

How will *we escape? I just want to shout,
"Help us! Please!"

I have an idea! Maybe if we *act calm, think things
through, and come up with a plan,
we will be okay.

77

Solve the Riddles

Riley's dad makes her laugh. He goofs around, makes funny faces, and tells corny jokes.

Solve the funny riddles. Fill in the missing letters to complete the nouns. Underline the other nouns in the riddle.

1. What has hands but cannot clap?
c l o c k

2. What gets wetter the more it dries? t o w e l

3. What's something you must keep after you give it?
p r o m i s e

4. What's full of holes but still holds water? s p o n g e

5. What has a floor but is not a room? o c e a n

6. What flies all day but never lands? f l a g

7. What can you catch but never throw? c o l d

8. Who can shave all day but still have a beard? b a r b e r

9. What must you break before you can use it? e g g

10. What is full of keys but can't open doors? p i a n o

11. What has one eye but can't see? ne e d l e

HINT A noun names a person, place, or thing.

78

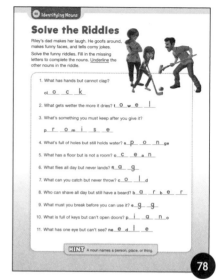

Word Ladder

Joy and Bing Bong are stuck at the bottom of the Memory Dump.

Build a noun ladder from the bottom to the top. Solve the clues. Save Joy and Bing Bong!

m a l l

b a l l

b u l l

b u l b

b u m p

l u m p

d u m p

A place to shop
Change one letter.

You throw it.
Change one letter.

A male cow
Change one letter.

Tulips and onions before they bloom
Change two letters.

A goose _____ shows you are cold.
Change one letter.

You may get one in your throat if you're about to cry.
Change one letter.

79

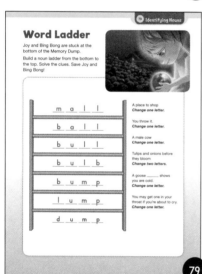

Maze

Oh no! Aunt Cass's cat, Mochi, is wandering away from the Lucky Cat Café.

The purple words above are proper nouns. Follow the proper nouns. Draw a path for Aunt Cass through the maze. Find Mochi!

Start

city
San Fransokyo
island
Akuma Island
Market Street
street
brother
Tadashi
neighbourhood
Yama
market
robot
Callaghan
professor
alley
headquarters
Finish

HINT Proper nouns are the names of specific things. They begin with capital letters.

80

Silly Sentences

Tadashi builds Baymax, a nursing robot, because he wants to help people.

If you could build a robot, what would it do? How would you introduce it to people?

Hello! I am *Nina (your name), a *young (adjective)

scientist and inventor.

I am unveiling *Dancy (proper noun), the most *flexible (adjective)

robot ever created.

More powerful than *Twinkle Toes Tony (proper noun)!

*Dancy (proper noun) is designed to *jitterbug (verb)

on *a disco ball (noun).

It can also *boogie (verb) into a *barnyard (noun).

Life in *Tango Town (place name) will never be the same!

HINT Make your story as silly as possible. Fill in the words before reading the rest of the sentence.

81

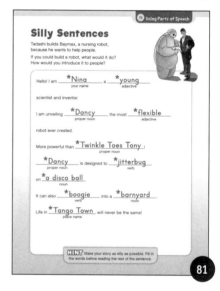

Fill In the Blanks

Riley's mom has something important to tell her about their move to San Francisco.

Fill in the missing verbs. See what Riley's mom wants to say. Use the words from the Word Bank.

Word Bank
announces   explains   is saying
enters   settles   surprises   thanks

1. Riley's mom e n t e r s Riley's bedroom.

2. Riley i s ready to hear more bad news, but her mom
s u r p r i s e s her.

3. Her mom s e t t l e s on the floor beside Riley's sleeping bag.

4. She a n n o u n c e s that she is very proud of Riley.

5. She e x p l a i n s that she has noticed how hard Riley is trying to be happy in their new home.

6. She t h a n k s Riley before
s a y i n g good night.

HINT Look at the number of letter spaces for each word.

82

Crack the Code

One of Riley's special memories is the first time she skated. She wobbled and slipped on the ice.

The purple words above are past tense verbs. Crack the code to discover the past tense verbs that make up more of Riley's memories.

Letter Code

a	b	c	d	e	f	g	h	i	j	k	l	m
1	2	3	4	5	6	7	8	9	10	11	12	13

n	o	p	q	r	s	t	u	v	w	x	y	z
14	15	16	17	18	19	20	21	22	23	24	25	26

1. When Riley t a s t e d broccoli for the first
   20 1 19 20 5 4
time, she thought it was disgusting.

2. When she s c o r e d her first goal, it was
   19 3 15 18 5 4
the most exciting thing ever.

3. Riley l o v e d playing with Bing Bong in their
   12 15 22 5 4
imaginary band.

4. She p l a y e d the pots and pans like drums.
   16 12 1 25 5 4

5. When Riley j o k e d with her friend Meg,
   10 15 11 5 4
she l a u g h e d so hard.
   12 1 21 7 8 5 4

HINT The past tense of a verb is often formed by adding -ed or -d (when the words end in an e).

83

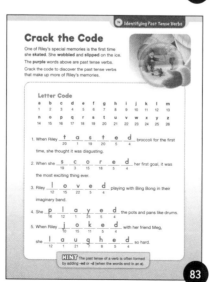

Crossword

The Big Hero 6 team is tense! They don't know if they'll be able to outsmart Yokai and his mind-controlled microbots.

Complete the crossword. Figure out which verb tense is needed. Some letters have been placed for you.

W A M
A R
L C A L L E D
O K
W A S E
A T R I E D
S

Across

2. This year, I _____ eight years old. (am / was)

4. My friend _____ me today. (call / called)

5. Last year, I _____ seven years old. (am / was)

6. Last week, I _____ karate. (try / tried)

Down

1. Yesterday, I _____ to school. (walk / walked)

2. Today, we _____ having spaghetti for dinner. (are / were)

3. Today, I _____ a quarter. (lose / lost)

5. My birthday _____ last month. (is / was)

84

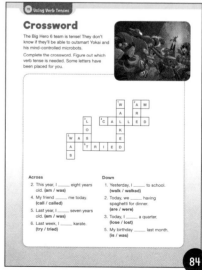

108

*Sample answers provided.

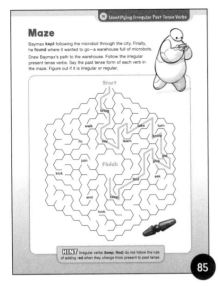

Maze

Baymax **kept** following the microbot through the city. Finally, he **found** where it wanted to go—a warehouse full of microbots.

Draw Baymax's path to the warehouse. Follow the irregular present tense verbs. Say the past tense form of each verb in the maze. Figure out if it is irregular or regular.

Start

bring
walk · take · turn
fix · say · learn · know
join · Finish · get · give
kick · find · ask
send · keep
look

HINT Irregular verbs (**keep, find**) do not follow the rule of adding **-ed** when they change from present to past tense.

85

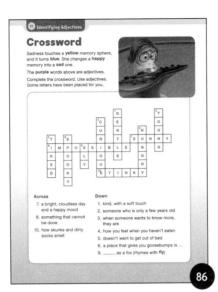

Crossword

Sadness touches a **yellow** memory sphere, and it turns **blue**. She changes a **happy** memory into a **sad** one.

The **purple** words above are adjectives.
Complete the crossword. Use adjectives. Some letters have been placed for you.

Across
7. a bright, cloudless day and a happy mood
8. something that cannot be done
10. how skunks and dirty socks smell

Down
1. kind, with a soft touch
2. someone who is only a few years old
3. when someone wants to know more, they are
4. how you feel when you haven't eaten
5. doesn't want to get out of bed
6. a place that gives you goosebumps is ...
9. ____ as a fox (rhymes with **fly**)

86

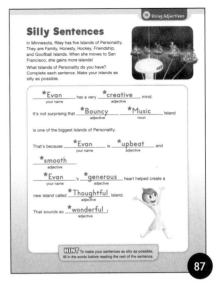

Silly Sentences

In Minnesota, Riley has five Islands of Personality. They are Family, Honesty, Hockey, Friendship, and Goofball Islands. When she moves to San Francisco, she gains more islands!
What Islands of Personality do you have?
Complete each sentence. Make your islands as silly as possible.

*Evan (your name) has a very *creative (adjective) mind.

It's not surprising that *Bouncy (adjective) *Music (noun) Island

is one of the biggest Islands of Personality.

That's because *Evan (your name) is *upbeat (adjective) and

*smooth (adjective)

*Evan (your name) 's *generous (adjective) heart helped create a

new island called *Thoughtful (adjective) Island.

That sounds so *wonderful (adjective)

HINT To make your sentences as silly as possible, fill in the words before reading the rest of the sentence.

87

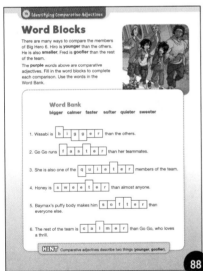

Word Blocks

There are many ways to compare the members of Big Hero 6. Hiro is **younger** than the others. He is also **smaller**. Fred is **goofier** than the rest of the team.

The **purple** words above are comparative adjectives. Fill in the word blocks to complete each comparison. Use the words in the Word Bank.

Word Bank
bigger calmer faster softer quieter sweeter

1. Wasabi is b i g g e r than the others.

2. Go Go runs f a s t e r than her teammates.

3. She is also one of the q u i e t e r members of the team.

4. Honey is s w e e t e r than almost anyone.

5. Baymax's puffy body makes him s o f t e r than everyone else.

6. The rest of the team is c a l m e r than Go Go, who loves a thrill.

HINT Comparative adjectives describe two things (**younger, goofier**).

88

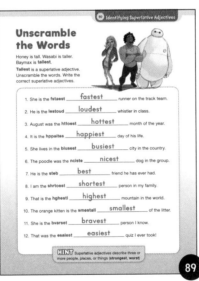

Unscramble the Words

Honey is tall. Wasabi is taller. Baymax is **tallest**.

Tallest is a superlative adjective. Unscramble the words. Write the correct superlative adjectives.

1. She is the **fstaest** ___fastest___ runner on the track team.
2. He is the **lestoud** ___loudest___ whistler in class.
3. August was the **httoest** ___hottest___ month of the year.
4. It is the **hppaitse** ___happiest___ day of his life.
5. She lives in the **bluesst** ___busiest___ city in the country.
6. The poodle was the **nciste** ___nicest___ dog in the group.
7. He is the **steb** ___best___ friend he has ever had.
8. I am the **shrtoest** ___shortest___ person in my family.
9. That is the **hghestl** ___highest___ mountain in the world.
10. The orange kitten is the **smestall** ___smallest___ of the litter.
11. She is the **bvarest** ___bravest___ person I know.
12. That was the **esaiset** ___easiest___ quiz I ever took!

HINT Superlative adjectives describe three or more people, places, or things (**strongest, worst**).

89

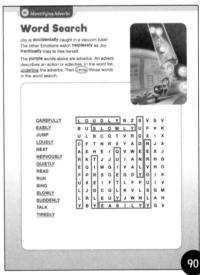

Word Search

Joy is **accidentally** caught in a vacuum tube! The other Emotions watch **helplessly** as Joy **frantically** tries to free herself.

The **purple** words above are adverbs. An adverb describes an action or adjective. In the word list, underline the adverbs. Then circle those words in the word search.

CAREFULLY
EASILY
JUMP
LOUDLY
NEAT
NERVOUSLY
QUIETLY
READ
RUN
SING
SLOWLY
SUDDENLY
TALK
TIREDLY

```
L O U D L Y B Z S V S V
B U S L O W L Y U F V K
U L B C Q T V R D X I X
C F T N R X Y A D N J A
A E H E I Q V W E E X J
R K T J J U I A N R H G
E Q I W G I V A L V H O
F P R S O E G D Y O I K
U X E I F T L F P U I V
L J D C Q L K V L S G M
L R L E U Y J W N L A H
Y B Y E A S I L Y V G Y
```

90

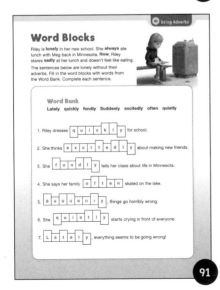

Word Blocks

Riley is **lonely** in her new school. She **always** ate lunch with Meg back in Minnesota. **Now**, Riley stares **sadly** at her lunch and doesn't feel like eating.

The sentences below are lonely without their adverbs. Fill in the word blocks with words from the Word Bank. Complete each sentence.

Word Bank
Lately quickly fondly Suddenly excitedly often quietly

1. Riley dresses q u i c k l y for school.

2. She thinks e x c i t e d l y about making new friends.

3. She f o n d l y tells her class about life in Minnesota.

4. She says her family o f t e n skated on the lake.

5. S u d d e n l y, things go horribly wrong.

6. She q u i e t l y starts crying in front of everyone.

7. L a t e l y, everything seems to be going wrong!

91

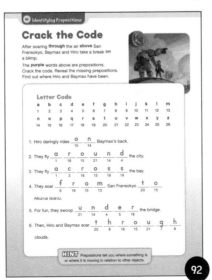

Crack the Code

After soaring **through** the air **above** San Fransokyo, Baymax and Hiro take a break **on** a blimp.

The **purple** words above are prepositions. Crack the code. Reveal the missing prepositions. Find out where Hiro and Baymax have been.

Letter Code
a	b	c	d	e	f	g	h	i	j	k	l	m
1	2	3	4	5	6	7	8	9	10	11	12	13

n	o	p	q	r	s	t	u	v	w	x	y	z
14	15	16	17	18	19	20	21	22	23	24	25	26

1. Hiro daringly rides o(15) n(14) Baymax's back.

2. They fly a(1) r(18) o(15) u(21) n(14) d(4) the city.

3. They fly a(1) c(3) r(18) o(15) s(19) s(19) the bay.

4. They soar f(6) r(18) o(15) m(13) San Fransokyo t(20) o(15) Akuma Island.

5. For fun, they swoop u(21) n(14) d(4) e(5) r(18) the bridge.

6. Then, Hiro and Baymax soar t(20) h(8) r(18) o(15) u(21) g(7) h(8) clouds.

HINT Prepositions tell you where something is or where it is moving in relation to other objects.

92

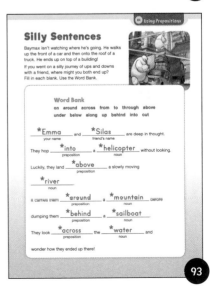

Silly Sentences

Baymax isn't watching where he's going. He walks up the front of a car and then onto the roof of a truck. He ends up on top of a building!
If you went on a silly journey of ups and downs with a friend, where might you both end up? Fill in each blank. Use the Word Bank.

Word Bank
on around across from to through above
under below along up behind into out

*Emma (your name) and *Silas (friend's name) are deep in thought.

They hop *into (preposition) a *helicopter (noun) without looking.

Luckily, they land *above (preposition) a slowly moving

*river (noun)

It carries them *around (preposition) a *mountain (noun) before

dumping them *behind (preposition) a *sailboat (noun)

They look *across (preposition) the *water (noun) and

wonder how they ended up there!

93

*Sample answers provided.

109

Answers

Using Conjunctions

Fill In the Blanks

Joy and Sadness work together to help Riley remember her core memories. Fill in each blank. Use or, but, or and to complete each sentence.

1. Riley tries to feel happy in San Francisco, __but__ she misses her life in Minnesota.

2. She can stay and be unhappy __or__ go back to Minnesota.

3. Riley starts to run away, __but__ she changes her mind.

4. She stands up in the bus __and__ tells the driver she wants to get off.

5. She loves her mom __and__ dad too much to leave.

6. They hug __and__ cry when she returns.

7. Riley and her parents feel sad because they miss their old life, __but__ they are happy they are together.

8. Riley soon joins a hockey team __and__ makes new friends.

9. If you moved to a new city, would you want to stay __or__ go?

94

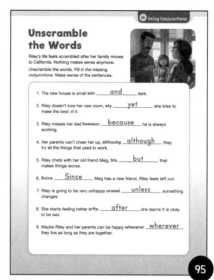

Using Conjunctions

Unscramble the Words

Riley's life feels scrambled after her family moves to California. Nothing makes sense anymore. Unscramble the words. Fill in the missing conjunctions. Make sense of the sentences.

1. The new house is small adn __and__ dark.

2. Riley doesn't love her new room, ety __yet__ she tries to make the best of it.

3. Riley misses her dad bseeauc __because__ he is always working.

4. Her parents can't cheer her up, althouhg __although__ they try all the things that used to work.

5. Riley chats with her old friend Meg, btu __but__ that makes things worse.

6. Snice __Since__ Meg has a new friend, Riley feels left out.

7. Riley is going to be very unhappy unssel __unless__ something changes.

8. She starts feeling better arfte __after__ she learns it is okay to be sad.

9. Maybe Riley and her parents can be happy wheverer __wherever__ they live as long as they are together.

95

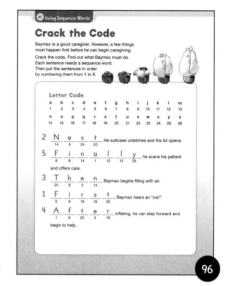

Using Sequence Words

Crack the Code

Baymax is a good caregiver. However, a few things must happen first before he can begin caregiving. Crack the code. Find out what Baymax must do. Each sentence needs a sequence word. Then put the sentences in order by numbering them from 1 to 5.

Letter Code

a	b	c	d	e	f	g	h	i	j	k	l	m
1	2	3	4	5	6	7	8	9	10	11	12	13

n	o	p	q	r	s	t	u	v	w	x	y	z
14	15	16	17	18	19	20	21	22	23	24	25	26

2 N e x t (14 5 24 20) his suitcase unlatches and the lid opens.

5 F i n a l l y (6 9 14 1 12 12 25) he scans his patient and offers care.

3 T h e n (20 8 5 14) Baymax begins filling with air.

1 F i r s t (6 9 18 19 20) Baymax hears an "ow!"

4 A f t e r (1 6 20 5 18) inflating, he can step forward and begin to help.

96

Writing Rhymes

Fill In the Blanks

Hiro never gives up on his invention. Because of his determination, he and the microbots receive thunderous applause at the Tech Showcase. Sadly, the person who wrote these rhymes gave up. Fill in the blanks to finish the rhymes. Use the words in the Word Bank.

Word Bank
easy early quit roughest blue

Just when things are at their toughest,

When your ideas are at their __roughest__

When you can't seem to make things fit,

It's the worst time for you to __quit__

You have to push and struggle through,

Frustration, doubt, and feeling __blue__

It won't be simple, fun, or __easy__

In fact, it just might make you queasy.

But if you give up and quit too __early__

Chances are you'll fail big, surely.

97

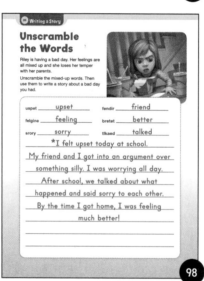

Writing a Story

Unscramble the Words

Riley is having a bad day. Her feelings are all mixed up and she loses her temper with her parents. Unscramble the mixed-up words. Then use them to write a story about a bad day you had.

uspet	upset	fendir	friend
felgine	feeling	bretet	better
srory	sorry	tlkaed	talked

*I felt upset today at school. My friend and I got into an argument over something silly. I was worrying all day. After school, we talked about what happened and said sorry to each other. By the time I got home, I was feeling much better!

98

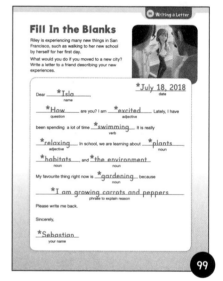

Writing a Letter

Fill In the Blanks

Riley is experiencing many new things in San Francisco, such as walking to her new school by herself for her first day.
What would you do if you moved to a new city? Write a letter to a friend describing your new experiences.

Dear *Isla (name)   *July 18, 2018 (date)

*How (question) are you? I am *excited (adjective) Lately, I have been spending a lot of time *swimming (verb) It is really *relaxing (adjective) In school, we are learning about *plants (noun) *habitats (noun) and *the environment (noun)

My favourite thing right now is *gardening (noun) because *I am growing carrots and peppers (phrase to explain reason)

Please write me back.

Sincerely,

*Sebastian (your name)

99

110

Cut out these flash cards. Use them to practise reading and writing.

magnets

chemicals

structures

strong

load

form

force

motion

friction

materials

matter

objects

shape

weight

stable

propel

movement

tension

Cut out these flash cards. Use them to practise reading and writing

Cut out these flash cards. Use them to practise reading and writing.

gravity

energy

urban

community

government

vote

population

transportation

climate

resources	voice	rural
industry	decisions	kinetic
factory	citizen	pulls

Cut out these flash cards. Use them to practice reading and writing.

recreation

intelligent

heroic

foe

destroy

wealthy

furious

nervously

suddenly

brave

smart

farmland

rich

ruin

enemy

tiredly

carefully

outraged

Congratulations

_____!
Print your name.

You have finished the
Brain Boost learning path.
Way to go!